D1083391

Kahn & Selesnick
Death of Actaeon

Death of Actaeon

Kahn & Selesnick

The air in the train was close and stuffy. Orlofsky had a catalogue from the National Gallery in his lap, opened to a reproduction of Titian's *Death of Actaeon*. In this painting, the goddess Diana shoots the naked trespasser with an arrow while he turns into stag and is devoured by her hounds. In our bags were a pair of enormous antlers; we intended to attach these to Orlofsky's head and set him loose onto Exmoor. Across the aisle, I noticed that a rather handsome, statuesque woman seemed to be showing undue interest in Orlofsky's reading material. She asked if that was Titian's Actaeon. Orlofsky blushed and nodded – he often couldn't communicate verbally with strangers without recourse to grunts and barks. The woman got up, sat down across from us, and leaned in conspiratorially: 'Did you know that I am related to Actaeon?' This flirtatious remark was aimed pointedly at Orlofsky. I could almost feel the beads of sweat oozing from his pores; an unpleasant musk suddenly pervaded the air about us. She continued: she had been a normal, healthy child, but one morning, not long after the first bloods, she awoke in a sea of feathers, her pillow torn. Her head felt different, and reaching up, she felt two sharp protrusions growing from her skull. She had cried out, and her mother had rushed into the room. Taking her daughter's hands in hers, her mother had explained that she was not like other people; she was special, her father had been a stag from the moorland. But hadn't daddy run off to Australia with a poetess? 'No sweetheart,' she said. Her mother told her that she would file down the little horns – it would be painful, but she would learn to manage;

her mother had then taken her hand and lifted it to her own scalp, and sure enough, she could feel small, bony nubs, worn smooth by years under the rasp. Lastly, her mother had said that although she would have boyfriends when she was grown up, one day, many years from now… this was left in the air, like a threat. After university, she moved to London to pursue the theatre; her mother had passed away, but she had kept their small cottage by the River Exe. One day, without being quite sure why, she stopped filing the horns. Within a week she had grown a large set of antlers; these were accompanied by dark, unsettling urges. She had boarded a train for Somerset, her enormous horns on full display to the other passengers. 'Do you know what it's like to be taken for a goddess?' she asked us, an almost wistful expression on her face. (Orlofsky nodded vigorously, as if for all the world he had been waiting for someone to ask him just this question. Absurd.) When she arrived she went out onto the moor. It was dusk and the deer were rutting. She heard a certain bark, and something had risen up in her throat, an orgasmic grunt, heavy and other-worldly; a response came back through the heady night air, and she returned to the cottage in a kind of trance. She knew, without knowing how, that she had arranged a rendezvous for the following evening, where the woodland met the moors. The next day, twilight fell and she went to the meeting place in her best dress; the horizon was the colour of an orange rind, the zenith dark blue and starry. As she walked through the heather, something struck her as wrong – there was a smell of death and excrement in the air. Near the wood's edge, she found him – her stag – lying in a pool of his own blood, a wound in his side, but still breathing. Their antlers had clacked as she threw her arms around his neck, her cold tears streaming down his reeking fur. Moments later she heard the baying of the hounds and fled for her life, not stopping until she had locked the door of the cottage behind her. Since that day, she kept her horns filed down to the skull. For a moment I feared she might take Orlofsky's sweaty paw and place it on her head, but instead she finally introduced herself: her name was Lulu, and she asked if she might accompany us on our expedition. We would be delighted, I had said, but as she gathered her luggage and put it with our own, I noticed with unease what appeared to be the outline of an archer's bow in one of her bags...

Wildfire: Eight years old at 3am

Tom Walsh

You're only eight years old but know a lot more than your parents or teachers give you credit for. Like you found the empty bags of Easter candy in the wastebasket a week before the Easter bunny came and now you're the one keeping that secret alive. Or that you saw Miss Emery give Johnny Doyle extra points on his tests because he's her nephew. It's 2020 people, and you know a lot more than they did at eight. Heck, the internet wasn't even invented then and you know more about a smartphone than most adults ever will.

So when dad wakes you up in the middle of the night and says to get dressed for a little ride in the truck you know something's wrong. When he says you're making a special trip to Grandma Jane up in Eureka – at 3 am – you know he's covering up. Mom's up and stuffing random photos and papers and knick-knacks into a duffel bag. She says Grandma Jane hasn't seen them in a while so we're bringing them with us, but you know that makes no sense.

Jake-dog is barking from his cage in the pickup and when you ask why he's coming your parents just stare at each other for a second and don't say anything because you all know that Grandma Jane can't stand Jake-dog ever since he broke her special Hummel with his tail. Dad tells you to hustle up and grab some favourite toys and stuffed animals and stick them in the bag he shoves into your hand. You start to ask why but he says loudly 'just do it' then quickly says he's sorry and to just listen and get ready.

But the smell of smoke is thick in the air and the sky over the ridge is orange and flickering and you know there's a fire coming so you move quickly. But how many animals and games can fit in one plastic garbage bag and what about all the games in the basement and the Xbox and the rocks you collected in the Sierras last summer and the starfish from Hawaii that smelled so bad for a while but is now in a special case that you built yourself or the pine cone collection or the electronic dinosaur that Auntie Sue sent for Christmas or everything else? Your parents should really tell you what to grab because even though you see the orange glow getting brighter and hear the sirens down the valley they keep saying it's an adventure and really it's not it's a horrible dream that might be real and have a really bad ending if you're up at Grandma Jane's and the flames come up and over the ridge and burn the house and the barn – what about the goats?! – and your bike and all the stuff laying in the yard around the swings that you only now just thought of and they haven't said anything about collecting and hauling with you so are they just going to let all that stuff burn?

And you think all of this so fast and still haven't put but two animals in the bag and your dad's picking you up with one strong arm and saying it's time to leave and you look back and see Goldie the Bear sitting on your rocking chair and scream 'Goldie Bear' even though you don't want to sound like a scared kid that needs to be told that everything's going to be OK and Dad grabs Goldie in his other hand and next thing you're in the truck and Jake-dog is still barking and mommy is crying and she never cries and you're driving away and the trees on the ridge line burst into flame and the smoke tastes like badly charred barbecue and the fire trucks along the roadside make red and white kaleidoscopes in the night.

And you're just eight years old but you know too much already and you know this is just the start.

the river

adrienne maree brown

something in the river haunted the island between the city and the border. she felt it, when she was on the waves in the little boat. she didn't say anything, because what could be said, and to whom?

but she felt it. and she felt it growing.

made a sort of sense to her that something would grow there. nuf things went in for something to have created itself down there.

she was a water woman, had learned to boat as she learned to walk, and felt rooted in the river. she'd learned from her grandfather, who'd told her his life lessons on the water. he'd said, 'black people come from a big spacious place, under a great big sky. this little country here, we have to fight for any inches we get. but the water has always helped us get free one way or another.'

sunny days, she took paying passengers over by the belle isle bridge to see the cars in the water. mostly, you couldn't see anything. but sometimes, you'd catch a glimpse of something shiny, metal, not of the river – something big and swallowed, that had a colour of cherry red, of 1964 american-made dream.

these days, the river felt like it had back then, a little too swollen, too active, too attentive.

too many days, she sat behind the wheel of the little boat, dialling down her apprehension. she felt a restlessness in the weeds and shadows that held detroit together. belle isle, an overgrown island, housed the ruins of a zoo, an aquarium, a conservatory, and the old yacht club. down the way were the abandoned, squatted towers of the renaissance centre, the tallest ode to economic crisis in the world.

she had been born not too far from the river, chalmers, on the east side. as a child she played along the river banks. she could remember when a black person could only dock a boat at one black-owned harbour. she remembered it because all she'd ever wanted was to be on that river, especially after her grandfather passed. when she was old enough, she'd purchased the little boat, motor awkward on its backside, and named her *bessie* after her mama. her mama had taught her important things: how to love detroit, that gardening in their backyard was not a hobby but a strategy, and to never trust a man for the long haul.

mostly, she'd listened to her mama. and when she'd gone astray, she'd always been able to return to the river.

now she was 43, and the river was freedom. in that boat she felt liberated all day. she loved to anchor near the underground railroad memorial and imagine runaway slaves standing on one bank and how good – terrifying, but good – that water must have felt, under the boat, or all over the skin, or frozen under the feet.

this was a good river for boating. you wouldn't jump in for any money. no one would.

she felt the same way about eating out of the river, but it was a hungry time. that morning she'd watched a fisherman reel in something, slow, like he didn't care at all. what he pulled up, a long slender fish, had an oily sheen on its scales. she'd tried to catch his eye with her disgust, offer a side eye warning to this stranger, but he turned with his catch, headed for the ice box.

she was aware of herself as a kind of outsider. she loved the city desperately and the people in it. but she mostly loved them from her boat. lately she wore her overalls, kept her greying hair short and natural, her sentences short. her routine didn't involve too many humans. when she tried to speak, even small talk, there was so much sadness and grief in her mouth for the city disappearing before her eyes that it got hard to breathe.

next time she was out on the water, on a stretch just east of chene park, she watched two babies on the rocks by the river, daring each other to get closer. the mothers were in deep and focussed gossip, while also minding a grill that uttered a gorgeous smell over the river waves. the waves were moving aggressive today, and she wanted to yell to the babies or the mamas but couldn't get the words together.

you can't yell just any old thing in detroit. you have to get it right. folks remember.

as she watched, one baby touched his bare toe in, his trembling ashy mocha body stretched out into the rippling nuclear aquamarine green surface. then suddenly he jumped up and backed away from the river, spooked in every limb. he took off running past his friend, all the way to his mama's thighs, which he grabbed and buried himself in, babbling incoherent confessions to her flesh.

the mother didn't skip a beat or a word, just brushed him aside, ignoring his warning.

she didn't judge that mama, though. times were beyond tough in detroit. a moment to pause, to vent, to sit by the river and just talk, that was a rare and precious thing.

off the river, out of the water, she found herself in an old friend's music studio, singing her prettiest sounds into his machines. he was as odd and solitary as she was, known for his madness, his intimate marrow-deep knowledge of the city, and his musical genius.

she asked him: *what's up with the river?*

he laughed first. she didn't ask why.

here is what he said: *your river? man, detroit is in that river. The whole river and the parts of the river. certain parts, it's like a ancestral burying ground. it's like a holy vortex of energy.*

like past the island? in the deep shits where them barges plow through? that was the hiding place, that was where you went if you loose tongue about the wrong thing or the wrong people. man, all kinds of sparkling souls been weighted down all the way into the mud in there. s'why some folks won't anchor with the city in view. might hook someone before they ghost! takes a while to become a proper ghost.

he left it at that.

she didn't agree with his theory. didn't feel dead, what she felt in the river. felt other. felt alive and other.

peak of the summer was scorch that year. the city could barely get dressed. the few people with jobs sat in icy offices watching the world waver outside. people without jobs survived in a variety of ways that all felt like punishment in the heat.

seemed like every morning there'd be bodies, folks who'd lost darwinian struggles during the sweaty night. bodies by the only over-night shelter, bodies in the fake downtown garden sponsored by coca-cola, bodies in potholes on streets strung with christmas lights because the broke city turned off the streetlights.

late one sunday afternoon, after three weddings took place on the island, she heard a message come over the river radio: four pale bodies found floating in the surrounding river, on the far side. she tracked the story throughout the day. upon being dragged out of the water and onto the soil by gloved official hands, it was clear that the bodies, of two adults and two teenagers, were recently dead, hardly bloated, each one bruised as if they'd been in a massive strug-gle before the toxic river filled their lungs.

they were from pennsylvania.

on monday she motored past the spot she'd heard the coast guard going on about over the radio. the water was moving about itself, swirling without reason. she shook her head, knowing truths that couldn't be spoken aloud were getting out of hand.

she tried for years to keep an open heart to the new folks, most of them white. the city needed people to live in it and job creation, right? and some of these new folk seemed to really care.

but it could harden her heart a little each day, to see people showing up all the time with jobs, or making new work for themselves and
their friends, while folks born and raised here couldn't make a
living, couldn't get investors for business. she heard entrepreneurs on
the news speak of detroit as this exciting new blank canvas. she
wondered if the new folks just couldn't see all the people there, the
signs everywhere that there was history and there was a people still
living all over that canvas.

the next tragedy came tuesday, when a passel of new local hipsters
were out at the island's un-secret swimming spot on an inner water-
way of belle isle. this tragedy didn't start with screams, but that was
the first thing she heard – a wild cacophony of screaming through the
thick reeds.

by the time she doubled back to the sliver entrance of the water-
way and made it to the place of the screaming sounds, there was just
a whimper, just one whimpering white kid and an island patrol,
staring into the water.

she called out: *what happened?*

the patrol, a white kid himself, looked up, terrified and incredulous
and trying to be in control. *well, some kids were swimming out here.
now they're missing, and this one says a wave ate them!*

the kid turned away from the river briefly to look up at the patrol,
slack-mouthed and betrayed. then the damp confused face turned to
her and pointed at the water: *it took them.*

she looked over the side of the boat then, down into the shallows
and seaweed. the water and weeds moved innocently enough, but
there were telltale signs of guilt: a mangled pair of aviator glasses,
three strips of natty red board shorts, the back half of a navy-striped
tom's shoe, a tangle of bikini, and an unlikely pile of clean new bones
of various lengths and origins.

she gathered these troubled spoils with her net, clamping her
mouth down against the lie 'I told you so,' cause who had she told?

and even now, as more kinds of police and coast guard showed up, what was there to say?

something impossible was happening.

she felt bad for these hipsters. she knew some of their kind from her favourite bars in the city and had never had a bad experience with any of them. she had taken boatloads of them on her river tours over the years. it wasn't their fault there were so many of them. hipsters and entrepreneurs were complicated locusts. they ate up everything in sight, but they meant well.

they should have shut down the island then, but these island bodies were only a small percentage of the bodies of summer, most of them stabbed, shot, strangled, stomped, starved. authorities half-heartedly posted ambiguous warning flyers around the island as swimmers, couples strolling on the river walk paths, and riverside picnickers went missing without explanation.

no one else seemed to notice that the bodies the river was taking that summer were not the bodies of detroiters. perhaps because it was a diverse body of people, all ages, all races. all folks who had come more recently, drawn by the promise of empty land and easy business, the opportunity available among the ruins of other peoples' lives.

she wasn't much on politics, but she hated the shifts in the city, the way it was fading as it filled with people who didn't know how to see it. she knew what was coming, what always came with pioneers: strip malls and sameness. she'd seen it nuff times.

so even though the river was getting dangerous, she didn't take it personally.

she hated strip malls too.

then something happened that got folks' attention.

the mayor's house was a mansion with a massive yard and covered dock on the river, overlooking the midwestern jungle of belle isle, and farther on, the shore of gentle canada.

this was the third consecutive white mayor of the great black city, this one born in grand rapids, raised in new york, and appointed by the governor. he'd entered office with economic promises on his lips, as usual, but so far he had just closed a few schools and added a third incinerator tower to expand detroit's growing industry as leading trash processor of north america.

the mayor had to entertain at home a few times a year, and his wife's job was to orchestrate elegance using the mansion as the back-drop. people came, oohed and aahed, and then left the big empty place to the couple. based on the light patterns she observed through the windows on her evening boat rides, she suspected the two spent most of their time out of the public eye happily withdrawn to oppo-site wings.

she brought the boat past the yard and covered dock every time she was out circling the island looking for sunset. as the summer had gone on, island disappearances had put the spook in her completely, and she circled farther and farther from the island's shores, closer and closer to the city.

which meant that on the evening of the mayor's august cocktail party, she was close to his yard. close enough to see it happen.

dozens of people coated the yard with false laughter, posing for cameras they each assumed were pointed in their direction. members of the press were there, marking themselves with cameras and tablets and smartphones, with the air of journalists covering something relevant. the mayor was aiming for dapper, a rose in his lapel.

as she drifted through the water, leaving no wake, the waves started to swell erratically. in just a few moments, the water began thrashing wildly, bucking her. it deluged the front of her little boat as she tried to find an angle to cut through. looking around, she saw no clear source of disruption, just a single line of waves moving out from the island behind her, clear as a moonbeam on a midnight sea.

she doubled the boat around until she was out of the waves, marvelling at how the water could be smooth just twenty feet east.

she looked back and saw that the waves continued to rise and roll, smacking against the wall that lined the mayor's yard.

the guests, oblivious to the phenomenon, shouted stories at each other and heimlich-manoeuvered belly laughter over the sound of an elevator jazz ensemble.

again she felt the urge to warn them, and again she couldn't think of what to say. could anyone else even see the clean line of rising waves? maybe all this time alone on the boat was warping her mind.

as she turned to move along with her boat, feeling the quiet edge of sanity, the elevator music stopped, and she heard the thumping of a microphone being tested. there he was, slick, flushed, wide and smiling. he stood on a little platform with his back to the river, his guests and their champagne flutes all turned toward him. the media elbowed each other half-heartedly, trying to manifest an interesting shot.

that's when it happened.

first thing was a shudder, just a bit bigger than the quake of summer 2010 which had shut down work on both sides of the river. and then one solitary and massive wave, a sickly bright green whip up out of the blue river, headed toward the mayor's back.

words were coming out her mouth, incredulous screams twisted with a certain glee: *the island's coming! the river is going to eat all you carpetbaggers right up!*

when she heard what she was saying she slapped her hand over her mouth, ashamed, but no one even looked in her direction. and if they had they would have seen naught but an old black water woman, alone in a boat.

the wave was over the yard before the guests noticed it, looking up with grins frozen on their faces. it looked like a trick, an illusion. the mayor laughed at their faces before realising with an animated double take that there was something behind him.

as she watched, the wave crashed over the fence, the covered dock, the mayor, the guests, and the press, hitting the house with its full force. with a start, a gasp of awe, she saw that the wave was no wider than the house.

nothing else was even wet.

the wave receded as fast as it had come. guests sprawled in all manner of positions, river water dripping down their supine bodies, some tossed through windows of the house, a few in the pear tree down the yard.

frantically, as humans do after an incident, they started checking themselves and telling the story of what had just happened. press people lamented over their soaked equipment, guests straightened their business casual attire into wet order, and security detail blew their cover as they desperately looked for the mayor.

she felt the buoys on the side of her boat gently bump up against the river wall and realised that her jaw had dropped and her hands fallen from the wheel. the water now was utterly calm in every direction.

still shocked, she gunned the engine gently back toward the mansion.

the mayor was nowhere to be seen. nor was his wife. and others were missing. she could see the smallness of the remaining guests. all along the fence was party detritus, similar to that left by the swallowed hipsters. heeled shoes, pieces of dresses and slacks. on the surface of the water near the mansion, phones and cameras floated.

on the podium, the rose from the mayor's lapel lay, looking as if it had just bloomed.

the city tried to contain the story, but too many journalists had been knocked about in the wave, felt the strange all-powerful nature of it, saw the post-tsunami yard full of only people like themselves, from detroit.

plus the mayor was gone.

the crazy, impossible story made it to the public, and the public panicked.

she watched the island harbour empty out, the island officially closed with cement blockades across the only bridge linking it to the city. the newly sworn-in mayor was a local who had been involved in local gardening work, one of the only people willing to step up into the role. he said this was an opportunity, wrapped in a crisis, to take the city back.

she felt the population of the city diminish as investors and pioneers packed up, looking for fertile new ground.

and she noticed who stayed, and it was the same people who had always been there. a little unsure of the future maybe, but too deeply rooted to move anywhere quickly. for the first time in a long time, she knew what to say.

it never did touch us y'know. maybe, maybe it's a funny way to do it, but maybe it's a good thing we got our city back?

and folks listened, shaking their heads as they tried to understand, while their mouths agreed: *it ain't how I'd have done it, but the thing is done.*

she still went out in her boat, looking over the edges near the island, searching inside the river, which was her most constant companion, for some clue, some explanation. and every now and then, squinting against the sun's reflection, she'd see through the blue, something swallowed, caught, held down so the city could survive. something that never died.

something alive.

Illustration by **Johanna Lohrengel**

Three Buzzing Boys

Julia Blackburn

One of these boys died more than two hundred and fifty years ago, the second only lived within the pages of a fairy tale, but I did meet the third, Dominique, while I was on holiday in a mountain village in the south of France. Actually it was his mother I met, although he was always there, sitting close beside her and never speaking but buzzing softly to himself like a somnambulant bee.

'He sleeps a lot close to the fire in the winter,' his mother said, 'because he doesn't like the cold. But he wakes up when it gets warm, don't you Dominique?' and when he heard his name being spoken he opened his mouth to make a sound which was almost like laughter.

But now I'll begin with the fairy tale boy whose name was Hans.

His parents had always longed for children and one day his father said, 'I want a child of my own, even if it's only a hedgehog!' And with the logic of such a wish, his wife duly gave birth to a creature whose lower half was human, while his upper half was covered in sharp prickles.

They called the boy Hans My Hedgehog because that was what he most resembled and they made him a bed of straw behind the stove, because he couldn't sleep in an ordinary bed. And so there he lay, drifting through the days and the nights in a dream of absence. Where there was skin on his body it was smudged grey with wood ash, while dried twigs and leaves lodged themselves among his prickles. Perhaps he was utterly silent, but I like to think he made a humming buzzing noise that was something between breathing and snoring.

Eight years went by like this, until the father announced he was going to the fair in town and he asked his hedgehog son what gift he wanted and Hans, who had never spoken before, replied, 'Bagpipes! I want bagpipes!' And so he was given this cumbersome and complicated instrument and he immediately knew how to produce the buzzing drone of air coursing through the pipes and all sorts of sweet melodies began to take shape.

Now that he had acquired a language, Hans was ready to leave home and so off he went into the world, carrying his bagpipes and riding on the back of a rooster. And because this is a fairy story in which the best things always happen to the youngest and especially the weakest child, he eventually wins the hand of a king's daughter, loses all his prickles on the night of his wedding and lives happily ever after.

The second buzzing boy appears so vividly in my mind's eye, it's as if I have sometimes seen him, pale and thin and determined, darting across a sunny field, although in fact I only know of him from the account written by the wonderful eighteenth century English naturalist, Gilbert White.

The boy isn't given a name, and Gilbert White explains nothing about the circumstances of his birth; just saying that the family lived close by in the same Hampshire village of Selbourne for a number of years and then they went away.

He says that during the cold months of the winter, the boy dozed away his time within his father's house, lying on the kitchen floor close to the fireplace and hardly ever moving from the chimney corner. But as soon as the weather grew mild with the approach of spring, he woke up from his hibernation and became alert and eager. And he began to make a humming noise with his lips; a sound that resembled the buzzing of bees.

We are in the middle of the eighteenth century and so when Bee Boy steps out of the front door of his family home, he enters a very different sort of countryside to the one we have grown accustomed to. In his journals and letters Gilbert White often mentions quite casually the sheer quantity of wildlife that surrounds him. On a warm day the air is thronging with insects and the village common is 'loud with the noise of bees.' Numerous brown owls sit hooting through the night in the walnut trees that grow close to his house, while several pairs of white owls 'haunt' his barn. He watches as swarms of house crickets run across the floor of his kitchen after dark, letting out two or three shrill notes of alarm if they are surprised by candle light. He speaks of the grasshopper larks whispering in his hedge and the fern owls and the nightingales that could be heard close by, singing together of an evening.

While we mourn the loss of almost all the thrushes in our gardens, he notes how these birds 'do great service in hunting-out the shell snails in the hedges and destroying them: the walls are covered with their shells.' And he writes of his brother in London, who nailed up empty scallops under the eaves of his house in South Lambeth and, 'within half an hour several pairs of house martins have started to use the shells as a base for their nests.' On one occasion he even gently complains that robin redbreasts keep entering all the rooms of his own house in the village of Selbourne, where they fly about, 'spoiling the furniture.'

Gilbert White was always fascinated by the way that living creatures, ourselves included, are able to adapt and make the best of their circumstances. A gypsy girl enters his garden during a heavy rain storm and makes herself a shelter from a piece of blanket among the hop vines and all on her own she gives birth to a little baby and then she has gone and no one knows where. An orphaned fawn is adopted by a herd of dairy cows who protect it from stray dogs and a cat that lost her kittens takes care of three little squirrels and nurses and suckles them, as if they were her real offspring.

In one of his letters he says that we are all in need of company of some sort or another and he tells the story of an acquaintance of his who kept a solitary horse and a solitary hen in an orchard and the unlikely pair became devoted friends, the hen keeping close to the horse and rubbing herself gently against his legs, the horse looking down at her with satisfaction and moving with 'the greatest caution and circumspection, lest he should trample on his diminutive companion.'

Alongside the gypsy girl and the lonely horse, the motherly cat and the noisy owls and the adventures of a lumbering tortoise called Timothy, Gilbert White describes the wordless boy who slept by the fire, until it was warm enough to step out into the spring landscape.

Buzzing like a bee, he went in search of bees and as soon as he found them he caught them in his bare hands and carefully removed the sting and sucked their little bodies to drink the sweetness they contained.

Sometimes he tucked a whole crowd of bees under his shirt, dozens of them trapped between the skin of his chest and the canopy of the cloth and there they buzzed about and tried to escape, but they never stung him.

When he came across villagers making the honey drink called *metheglin*, he would hum and buzz with excitement, hovering close and begging for a taste of bee wine and when he went to the bee gardens where they kept their rows of hives, he sat in front of these humming boxes and rapped with his finger on the wood so that the bees flew out in a thin angry column and then he could take them, one by one. Sometimes he even tipped the hives over to lift out the heavy combs dripping with honey and filled with bee larvae, the queen somewhere at the centre of her golden kingdom. And he ate the wax and all its contents and still he was not harmed. And he wasn't hated either, because everyone in the village seemed to be able to accept the presence of this strange child within their community and they adapted themselves to his ways, and gave him honey wine to drink and set the hives straight and life went on.

I suppose that when I imagine Bee Boy, it is really the French boy Dominique who I see. He was what used to be called moonstruck. His whole body seemed to be loose, as if the nuts and bolts of sinews and joints had never been tightened up in the right way and his head kept lolling to one side, while a little smile of benevolent confusion never left his face. He hadn't mastered the art of speaking but he made a continuous softly buzzing sound, as if the words were trapped inside his body and could find no means of escape .

His mother kept a tiny shop in the dark cellar of her house from where she sold honey from her beehives and fruit and vegetables from her garden: a few white fleshed peaches in a basket, a bunch of onions, a bunch of garlic.

Like many old people, she wanted to talk about the old days when she was young and the village was bustling with life. People lived on the land and harvested chestnuts from the forest, but what they specialised in was the cultivation of silkworm caterpillars. When you approached the village in the springtime, you could hear the sound of thousands of caterpillars chewing on mulberry leaves and when she said that I wondered if it was more of a caterpillar sound that her son Dominique was making.

The caterpillars were kept on special wooden stacks in the attic rooms of the big farmhouses, munching away from dawn until dusk and getting fatter and fatter until they were ready to spin their silken swaddling clothes.

Once they had completed this task, the days had to be carefully counted until just before the moth was ready to emerge and then the cocoons were plunged into boiling water. The woman said that a well-timed cocoon yielded a kilometre of spidery thread and she went rummaging through a cupboard at the back of the shop until she found one which she put in my hand so I could consider the unlikely miracle of such a length of silk being contained within such a tiny parcel. That was when Dominique leant forward and took the cocoon from me and lifted it up as if to put it in his mouth, but his mother stopped him just in time. She said payment was by the kilo, but you'd think such fragile things could never weigh anything, no matter how many were heaped up on the scales.

In those long-ago days the life cycle of the silk moth was the concern of the whole village and if a woman was pregnant or sick with fever, then she was chosen to wear a little cloth bag held with a ribbon around her neck and tucked safely between the soft cleavage of her bosom and the bag was filled with the glistening white eggs that were best hatched slightly above normal body heat.

Once the baby caterpillars were just beginning to emerge they were carried to the attic rooms and then it was important to keep absolutely still while they waved their querulous heads in search of green leaves and climbed the wooden stacks and established their position and began to eat.

The village was situated on the steep slopes of a hill and the mulberry trees grew in the valley near a stream that had never run dry not even in the hottest weather. Three times a day the women walked down the winding stone path to collect the mulberry leaves and then they walked back again as fast as they could, their bundles wilting in the sunlight.

The old woman said things had fallen apart very abruptly; imported silk was suddenly very cheap to buy and then to make matters worse all the mulberry trees in the region became diseased and many of them died and those that survived turned into straggling bushes.

So the attics were left empty and silent and no one spun the gossamer silk threads any more. 'And now,' she said, 'our children and grandchildren have all gone to the towns and the cities where they can find jobs and earn a decent living. There is only me and two other old women and three old men who are still here. And Dominique of course, because he can't leave.'

So there I was listening to an old woman talking and sometimes we drank sweet black coffee together and sometimes we just sat on rickety wooden chairs next to the little displays of fruit and vegetables and all the while Dominique was buzzing close beside his mother and whenever she mentioned him by name, he would erupt with the sound that was almost like laughter.

When I came to see her for the last time I brought her a box of soap as a gift and for Dominique I had a spotted handkerchief. I offered it to him and he grinned and took hold of it and rose to his feet and flapped his arms like wings as if he and the handkerchief were about to fly up to the ceiling and surprise us all.

His mother spoke to him in quite a sharp tone and with that he stopped flapping his arm-wings and returned to her side, the handkerchief on his lap.

I imagined Dominique curled up by the fire during the winter months, his skin blotched grey by the soft wood ash and hardly any separation between the days and the nights, but still in his own way safe and watched over and accepted for who he was.

This story is also available as an audio version read by the author.
See page 241 for more details, or visit dark-mountain.net/issue-18-fabula-audio

Killing Snakes

Conrad Shumaker

My father taught my brother and me to kill rattlesnakes when we were about seven or eight, about the same time we learned to drive a tractor and got our own horses. A shovel works best, he said. You get them to strike at the metal so they'll uncoil, or just knock them out of their coil, and then cut their heads off close to the poison sacs. It didn't really have to be too close, but it was neater that way, less like cutting them in half. We already knew enough not to touch the head part, since it could still bite. We believed the head would live till sunset, though Dad hadn't told us that.

He killed rattlers with his pistol, usually. It was always handy because he went around much of the time dressed like the cowboys you saw on *Rawhide* – not the fancy ones with pearl-handled guns and embroidered silver-trimmed vests but the trail hands with dusty brown boots and Levi's and a single wooden-handled revolver low on the hip where the right hand could get it on the way up.

He could dress that way because he had grown up dressed like that, and he made his living, or more often his debts, raising cattle and cotton. The boots and hat were for riding in the Arizona sun, working and branding cattle, moving them from one irrigated pasture to another. The pistol was for killing animals – rattlers that could bite calves or kids, jackrabbits that would eat the young cotton to the ground. Dad didn't like to kill the rabbits. I knew because he would always swear while he did it. 'Sons of bitches,' he'd say, 'why don't they just eat the goddamned alfalfa?' They twisted into the air when the bullets hit them, did crazy flips and usually hit the ground dead.

He didn't seem to mind killing the snakes. He'd shoot at their heads from a fair distance, then walk over to make sure the damage was enough. If we had ever thought of asking, we would have said that was right. In a box in my attic there are pictures of the three of us standing side by side – Dad, then me, then my younger brother – each of us in boots and hat and Levi's and cotton shirts with snaps instead of buttons, with three drawn pistols pointed at my mother, who was holding the camera. Rattlesnakes were part of that; they were everywhere – in the empty field behind the house, around the puddle of water that ran off the roof from our swamp cooler, sometimes even warming themselves on the concrete of our front porch, and we saw them simply as evil, or rather, as the potential danger that's always mixed with simple things like riding a horse or a bike or just opening a door.

I remember that once my brother and I were playing in a dry arroyo, caving fragile undercut banks just to watch the miniature landslide it made. We had stamped on a chunk of bank and slid down with it into the sand at the bottom in a thick cloud of dust, when we heard the dry buzz of a rattler. We froze, hoping that we weren't too close, fighting the urge to run out of the dust cloud, until finally we could see the snake coiled beside a large clod. It was grey-brown like the crumbled dirt, thick as my wrist, and as we began to throw rocks at it, it showed the pale pink inside of its mouth, the fangs erect and evil-looking.

We cut off the rattles with a sharp rock and walked home smiling, punching each other lightly on the shoulders, convinced that we were heroes, first for standing still in the choking dust and the buzz instead of panicking and maybe running onto the snake, and then for killing the snake with rocks instead of running a quarter of a mile to find a shovel and probably letting it escape. We didn't tell my father about it, though, because he would have said we were stupid for caving banks that way. My mother might have gotten upset and told us not to go there again. So we were silent heroes and felt good about that too.

So when my cousin from Phoenix came to visit us we decided to take him out to kill a rattler. My mother's sister was having 'troubles' again, and it looked like she and my cousin might have to stay for a while. We never knew just what troubles she had because she and my mother – who came from Michigan and was never in the cowboy pictures – would whisper in the kitchen washing dishes, and when we came in they would stop whispering and pretend to joke. We never asked my cousin what the troubles were. We didn't think we should ask about things that made mothers sound that way; I'm still a little scared by the sound women make whispering. We just decided that my cousin needed to kill a snake because he was nine and lived in Phoenix in a subdivision and wore shoes instead of boots and smoked cigarettes sometimes, and he hadn't killed anything even though he'd been to the farm more than once before. And we thought maybe killing a snake would make him feel better about the whispered things.

We picked up two shovels on the way out to the field behind the house, and then we looked in the likely places – among the cross ties piled haphazardly for use as future fence posts, under the scattered concrete blocks left over from building a new room on our adobe house, in the nests of dried cholla cactus drifted into arroyo eddies, the mesquite thickets near the dry river bed. Even though my cousin usually acted tough in a city way, saying 'shit' a lot and talking about Lucky Strikes and how he stole bubblegum from the Chinaman's store, we could see he was scared, and we yelled 'There's one!' at least six times before he finally stopped jumping when we did it. We found several lizards, a couple of scorpions and a toad, but there were no snakes.

It was hot, so we carried our shovels to the dry bed of the Santa Cruz River, which lay a few hundred yards behind our house, and dug down in the shade of a big mesquite until the hot white sand began to turn brown and cool, and then we took off our boots and shirts and pants and wrestled in the dampness until our backs and chests and legs were covered with sand and when we walked we could feel sand in the sweat between our buttocks. A branch of the mesquite we were playing under hung out over the riverbed, so we climbed up and jumped into the hole we had dug. The bark was dark and rough and had a spicy smell, and you could see little black ants with pointed abdomens held high running over it, and the wind from the jump would cool your hair for a second until you fell into the damp sand and rolled naked in its wet smell.

When the sun was nearly down a snake came out of the brush about fifty feet from our spot and we grabbed the shovels and ran to it, and it was a rattler, nearly three feet long. My cousin wanted to put his clothes on, or at least his shoes, but we said he could do it like he was and that would make it even better – we didn't know anyone who had killed a rattler naked before. So we showed him how to get the snake to uncoil, and he jabbed the tip of the shovel behind the flat triangular head, but he didn't push hard enough, and the snake rolled in the sand flashing its white belly with the straight narrow scales, rolled in agony and fear, it suddenly seemed to me, as the metal pushed against the base of its skull, and I said, 'Push hard, goddamnit!' and my cousin started to cry because he was leaning on the shovel and couldn't push hard enough against the soft sand, but he was afraid to let up because the snake was near his bare foot rolling and coiling, throwing its muscled useless body over the edge of the shovel, wrapping around the wood of the handle while the metal worked into its neck. And the rattle buzzing all the time like dry wind through cactus needles. I stepped on the top of the shovel blade and felt the scales and the muscle cool and smooth as polished living stone when the snake coiled its body around my bare ankle and then there was the pain as the rolled metal top of the shovel bit into my foot and at the same time a snip and the body twisted free and came

[29]

right off the sand, then rolled over showing white and grey and white and grey and the head on the other side of the shovel looking thin as paper and opening and closing, sand clinging to the pink inside where the fangs were, so it looked like the head was chewing the dark wet grains.

On the way home we told my cousin that he had done it, that he was a snake killer now, since I had just helped him a little bit. But I couldn't help thinking about the damp sand and the snake coming out into the cool evening and about the twisting, the trying to live, and I knew that something clear had blurred, like a picture that got left out in the sun.

This story is also available as an audio version read by the author.
See page 241 for more details, or visit dark-mountain.net/issue-18-fabula-audio

The Night Heron

Neale Inglenook

...what jellies of arrogance and terror
This earth has absorbed.

– Robinson Jeffers
Iona: The Graves of the Kings

It was after the whale-kill and his father's broken back that the old man led him up to the high point on the headland. First along a path stamped into the dune sand, until it gave out under a fissured granite escarpment. The old man went up through a cut in the rock and Harpen followed, over tumbled scree between narrowing walls.

They came to a ledge after some time climbing, and the old man stepped onto it and looked down at the village. Harpen mimicked him like a shadow.

Below them were the fractured knives of granite, and the runnelled sand with ant tracks across it, then the willows around the shallow fens splotched with bright algae. The brown domes like nut hulls discarded on a sandy midden, grey ferns of smoke growing from their chimneys. Black figures moved among the houses, tiny and lonely.

Beyond the village the undulant plain lay out to the feet of distant Mountains, slopes hazy and dim, brilliant snowy peaks. Clouds shuttling from the west across the sky over the pale sun.

The wind swept around the headland with the scent of wet salt and sea-wrack. The old man was still as a dolmen except for his white hair hovering like the wings of a gull. Harpen watching him from the corner of his eye, waiting for some sign.

He had been softening seal hides with his brothers when the old man had stepped out of the willows and said, 'Come.' Then he had turned to leave as though Harpen were already following. Harpen laid the hide on the pine pole frame, his palm up in apology. His twin brothers took the hide at either side and began rubbing it over the wooden rib as if he had never been there.

Finally the old man turned wordless to the stone and gripping his stout fingers into the crevices began to climb. Above them the broken peaks scratched the sky.

Higher up they came on the nests of seabirds, gulls flapping up into the gusts and crying shrill as they passed. Their eggs grey mounds in nests of dune sedge, the stone streaked white with their guano. A gull swung in and snapped at Harpen's ear, her battering wings. He pushed her off and pulled his hood over his head and kept going. This kind of climbing Harpen knew, from the egg harvest. But they were not here for food, that much he understood. He focussed on his hands on the rough stone, his toes finding their hold.

When they reached the heights the sun was already wan in the east. The shadows of the headland stretched back toward the plain. They came to a gap where the wind charged through, the old man hunching forward into it, gusts buffeting their hides. The rock walls opened out and suddenly the promontory dropped away sheer to the foaming breakwater. Below them the gulls wheeled on grey-tipped wings. Harpen tight in his gut, the height all wrong. Cold spray swept over his cheeks. Sea was an endless succession of whitecaps disappearing into the mist on the horizon.

The old man seemed to watch a line of pelicans skim the breaker crests. Then he turned and climbed a few more steps up a rise to a flat place below the highest peak.

As Harpen came up toward the little plateau he saw something there that did not belong to the granite. It was a slab, too regular and flat, though cracked through in several places and crumbling at the edges. It was not large – no wider than his arm span. In the broken corners Harpen saw round stones as if from a stream bed, and veins of something deep red and flaking.

The old man climbed onto the slab, and crawled toward the centre, where set in the stone was a little dome like a cake urchin. The dome was not stone nor shell – it was something else.

'Come here,' the old man said.

Harpen climbed slowly up beside him and looked down at the dome. Salt filigree grew over a surface the colour of sunset in a tide pool. The old man burnished the crystals away with his palm. In the fading light Harpen leaned in and saw the ghosts of symbols in a ring.

'You can touch it.'

Harpen rubbed this thumb across the surface. It was smooth as a tide rock, but somehow malleable, as though if he pressed hard enough he might leave his fingerprint.

'Can you make out the marks.'

Harpen looked again, but shook his head.

The old man nodded. 'Neither can I.'

He put his hands on the stone on either side of the dome.

'This was made by hands,' he said. 'There were symbols carved there to leave some message, but they have been wiped away by wind, by sand, by salt. And by our touch. Every touch takes something.'

Harpen looked at his hand and saw nothing there, no gold dust.

'Sea is relentless and will eat this marker and this headland in time.' The old man turned and looked out towards the sunset.

'To us,' he began after a moment, and his voice had changed, deepened like surf thunder so that Harpen knew he was speaking the words from the Book, '*the tide-worn cliff at the sea-gate a measure of continuance.*'

Old words, with many sounds. As usual he did not understand. The old man could look into the Book and know things, hear spirit voices, words no one else knew. This his fearful power. This he was teaching Sheath. Harpen could not help but think of her raven feather cloak brushing the back of his neck as she stepped past him in the meeting house, carrying the Book to the old man to read. Could the old man read Harpen like the Book, like Harpen looked at Clouds for the weather. Did he know Harpen's insides – the shaking yearning to touch the tender skin below Sheath's ear.

The wind keened in the crags over them. Harpen looking down toward the waves in fear that his feelings marked his face.

'How long has this cliff been here,' asked the old man.

Harpen glanced at him and away. Was it a trick, or a test. 'Ten lives,' he ventured, his voice pinched.

The old man gave a small smile. 'Could be. Could be a hundred lives. Forever. Could be our people have been here all that time.' He paused and breathed. 'But not so. Sea used to wash up here, all the way to Mountains' feet. And it was far away over there that our people used to live.'

The old man turned towards him. Harpen's chest shivered. None of this was normal, not climbing this high, not being alone with the old man, not having him speak in his ear. He turned and looked into the old man's single eye, not to seem afraid. It was deep-set in its hooded socket, the iris like wet serpentine. The other lid was sunken in, painted with seal oil and charcoal, but seemed to watch him still.

'There is something I need you to hear,' said the old man. 'Listen well now.'

Harpen gave a small nod, and the old man went on.

'Our ancestors were very powerful. Enough to change the face of the world. They numbered like krill, and they were good killers. Their feasts were mountains of kill and they feasted daily.'

He paused to let the thought sink to Harpen's gut.

'To do so much killing they had cunning, powerful weapons. Spears that could fly from here to the village. One person could wield the thunder of Clouds.'

Harpen looked out to the horizon, trying to see it, but this was a strange story.

'All their killing and eating made their villages grow and grow, until there was no space between them. They began to build house upon house, until they rose up into the sky, higher than this headland, you would never believe them. These *cities* the prophet speaks of in the Book. And they could make animals, huge birds they rode through the sky, and horses to ride over land, living boats that sailed themselves. They built them out of this.'

The old man pointed to the marker. 'This *metal*.'

Harpen felt plucked strings humming in his lungs, sharp and fibrous.

'Metal,' he said.

There were filaments of it kept in the sacred bundles, a remnant gnawed by the invisible teeth of the salt air. Only the old man and a few others handled them. They had to be understood to be touched. The other meaning was a person's power, what one gained by besting challenges, by making elegant tools, by taking animals, by defeating enemies.

The old man nodded looking at the waves. 'Two things made this power possible,' he said. 'One was the metal they dug from deep in the heart of Mountains. They melted it in their fires, hotter than you have ever seen. They bent it to their will.'

'The other thing was the oil of the dead. They made giant worms that ate down into Sea's bed, to find where the dead hide. They dredged up the sludge of death. It was what fuelled their fires to free metal from Mountains, and it was what made their creations live. They made the form of the bird, the form of the horse, and they poured the liquor of death into them. They made the forms of the dead dance again with the sludge of their spirits.'

Harpen felt the thrill of being let in on a secret, all mixed with bile in his gut. What else had they kept from him. All this could not be believed anyway. Great whales he had seen, but giant worms, and hand-made animals filled with the sludge of souls – he felt used, as if these stories were a way to hone him into something.

'Listen,' the old man said. 'You won't take what others say without thinking. Not bad. We have to know the world for ourselves. But there are some things you cannot see yet, and if you listen you may learn.'

The old man turned back towards the metal marker, its inscrutable signs. A gaggle of terns soared by battling each other for a mangled fish.

Harpen longed to be alone. Even away from the old man. Alone there were no more words. Words and words could lie, but Sea could not lie. She might surprise, but she had never made any promises, so she could not break them.

'This is what I want to say.' The old man put two fingers up and touched his empty eye socket. 'I see more than you know. I see your skill as a killer. A good skill – it feeds the people. And to kill is to see something, not the shadow of that thing. But it is not everything. The people long ago were cunning killers too. They lived close to death always. Its power moved their metal beasts, it warmed their houses all winter, it lit their nights blazing.

'But listen to this and see it, not its shadow. It was also their unravelling. They thought they could spear Clouds, grind down Mountains. They thought they could master death, but nothing masters death.

'Belief in your own metal beyond its truth will be the end of you. It closed down their world and sent all but us few to live in their oils under the earth, and it made Sea roll back and it emptied the land of animals and left all these things that make our lives hard, cold and sickness and darkness. That trail leads to scattered bones and empty wind.

'This is what I want you to hear.'

*

An evening before the equinox. Someone called at the door. His mother answered, then came to him and touched his shoulder while his father's pained face hung ashen across the hearth.

'The old man wants you,' his mother said, and Harpen put down the arrowhead he had been working out of sea glass.

Cypress trees hissed in a breeze and Clouds muffled the stars. There were hunters coming from the other houses, Harpen silent among them, walking steadily feeling the rocks and sand beneath the soles of his boots. They all made a line to the sweat house, and bowed down to go in the low entrance. Harpen, near the back of the line, put his forehead to the mud of the entryway and smelled the cold sweat and the damp rot of the soil.

He sat in the pine needles and looked at the faces of the hunters, lit by the small fire that fluttered in the pit, lines in them like cracking stone.

The old man sat opposite the door. His hands lay in his lap with a smoldering bundle of cedar incense. The smoke about him parted like a shroud as he leaned forward. Everyone went still, listening.

'There are hunters coming,' the old man said. 'They have already crossed the river.'

As if foretelling the weather. Harpen felt a quiver in the earth. He was too young, he was not supposed to be here. But the old man had said. His guts were knotting themselves like cordage around what he might do.

'They want what we have stored from the summer. They want to take what will give us life over the long dark. It's time to meet killer with killer,' the old man said to his lap, and lifted the incense. The grey smoke spilled upwards into the rafters.

The old man said, '*Wounds, bonds, limits, and pain.* We release you from these. Step into *the crystal-black water of an end.* Tread like night heron in dark pool, no ripple. Knife beak, red eye.'

Harpen stared into the fire. Shifting shapes of the future. Under him, the cold inertia of the great black lake within the earth. When he looked up the old man's one eye was on him. Smoke eddied between them.

'You are killers now,' the old man said.

*

Then his hands were his spear, they grew into the shaft of pine like knotting roots and he felt the bone point as if it were the tip of his finger. Crouched in a willow break under deep night. A breeze hissing in the leaves around him. Listening hard, blood drumming through his eyes searching the shadows upon shadows. The wind lulled and a twig snapped and his eyes swung and he stayed still and felt himself of a piece with willow branch and trunk.

Then through the sandy draw beside the willows came the shadow of a hunter, in dusky hides, a straight shock of hair to their shoulders, and in their hand was some weapon, a club or axe. They walked with their toes forward, so that their feet rolled down over sand and leaf and were near silent. But Harpen could hear, each grain grating, and he watched the shadow through slitted eyes.

The hunter came to a stop just down the draw, revolving like leaf on a slow stream. Harpen's pulse hammered wood in his ears. He tried to dream of being a willow. So still he might breathe once a season, drink water from deep in the ground.

Then the hunter turned away and began to move again. And it was the moment. A killer knows. Harpen leaping from cover threw his spear – it left his hand with a tiny snap like a tree limb breaking far away. The shadow turned at the sound, bringing their weapon to bear, but the spear stopped them hard as it went through their ribs. Harpen heard a gasp that did not come from their mouth. The two stood there face to face, the spear quivering between them. Harpen staring into their wide white eyes. It was the shadow that had stalked them and brought them down, sent them spinning off into the stillness of the black lake beneath the earth. Then the hunter tumbled, an unhinged weight falling heavy to the sand.

*

Later he went with the old man to the place of the killing. There the body lay drying in the sand, their hands curling, skin like a tanned hide. Mouth crusted, chips of grey teeth inset there. Sunken eyes. The spear growing from their chest like a canted sapling.

Harpen stood trembling in the sandy draw beside the old man. He did not know where to look. He did not want to look into the willows and see himself there waiting to kill.

Behind them came two cousins of Harpen's, Branch and Keel, woman and man. Both had killed before, he knew this. Never had he thought about what they must feel inside.

His cousins laid armloads of wood beside the corpse. More was needed – they went to get it without a word. Far off in the village, Harpen could hear the keening of the bereaved.

'This is the way it must be done,' the old man said. 'To keep our place in the world, and not be ground out of it. All things want to live. Today you and your family live, and they do not. We will burn the body, spear and all. The ashes will flow down to the roots of the willow, the coyote will scatter the bones.'

The old man looked at the side of Harpen's face. Harpen did not turn to him. After a time the old man left him there.

His cousins came back and began to stack the wood around the body, until there was a makeshift hut with the haft of the spear rising from its peak. Night speeding down from Mountains toward them.

They made fire with Keel's kit, and Branch placed the flaming tinder at the feet of the corpse, and laying her cheek to the sand blew until the tiny house began to burn.

His cousins stepped back. They seemed shades beside the life of the fire. The world closing in around it. The smell of smoking fat and

[39]

charred meat turned Harpen's stomach and he crouched, holding himself.

The leaning branches went to charcoal and collapsed inwards. The old man stepped into the burnishing firelight. He sat at Harpen's shoulder and began to sing an old song with words Harpen did not understand.

He sang for a long time. In the coals were the dark shapes of the bones. The skull with flames for hair.

At last the old man stopped his song and stood.

'Come away before it's all burned down,' he said.

He took Harpen's arm and pulled him upright and they turned towards the village. All across the hills, the pyres like flickering stars.

*

After the equinox the people went down into their houses, to emerge as little as possible until the spring. In the long nights of winter, every-one became lean and gaunt in the smoky shadows. They slept as much as they could, banked the fire and curled in their hides, ate one piece of seaweed at a time, waited for the cold to break.

In the dim house, in the smoke, where his family hunched to their work of softening hides, knapping tools, mending nets, there was a smell. A scent of sea-wrack and carrion. It followed him about the house and to bed and he could not lose it until he was out of the village and into the breath of Sea. He put his nose to his clothes, his boots; he pulled his hair around to his face, trying to suss it out. It did not seem to come from any particular place, but it wafted off of him, he was sure. There was something on him rotting.

He watched the faces of his parents, his brothers as he passed close by or when they lay down in bed. He looked for some slide of eye, head turning away. They must sense it, if it came off him this way. And sometimes the words of the Book crept through his mind, no comfort, mumbled prophecies...*the dark earth so shallow on the rock, gorged with bad meat...*

*

That winter he went snow-blind several times, so much time he spent on the ice. The bitter sunlight glanced off the brilliant snow and burnt with a chill heat. His eyes flared and his sight went white as if his pupils had been held to the very ice.

Still he needed to be out, in the clean air, Clouds coming and coming as if to cleanse the sky of any mote. There it was only the smell of the cold brine of Sea, the chill body of Clouds. Between them he became small, and all the sick tides of feeling in him that rose and filled his throat, they were also small, in proper proportion.

Those days he stood long over the breathing-hole of the seal, lost in the round blue depth. Spear poised. No thoughts. And when the seal came he did not miss. The point diving in. The blood spraying into the snow, the seal thrashing until he pulled it out onto the ice and cut its throat. Putting his mouth to the cut to drink the blood as he had been taught, not to waste. Bitter metal, steadily pumping into him. And then the walk back across the ice, the seal-corpse sliding behind him loose with death, onto the rocks of the beach, the hunched village looming, hazed by snows, iced-over doorways, wisps of grey smoke lost in the wind. Then there would be the cutting and preparing of the seal. But he would not eat, the blood was enough, what he drank on the ice, lips to the warm mouth of the knife cut, the seal's wet eye staring at the sky without comprehension.

*

His mother gave him a tonic of a wort weed. In the coals of the family hearth she heated stones and placed them in a wooden bowl full of water and the herb. Then she watched Harpen as he spooned it all out and ate the woody stalks now reawakened to a boiled green in the broth. His brothers' eyes were hooded and sullen where they hid in their bed. There was no hot broth made specially for them.

After these treatments, Harpen slept without dreams. He woke groggy, with the sense that he had been away on a long hunting trip and could not now remember where he had been. Even the heat of the broth was gone, a chill in his stomach. And no hours of day in the house, only an endless half-sleep, descending toward midwinter.

For a time after sleeping, the scent dissipated. All his senses felt blurred and distant, his fingers numb and fumbling, his eyes weeping. As if separated from the world by a skein of ice. It was perhaps two days when he did not smell even brine or wood-smoke. He sat in the hut in the fog of his thoughts, trying to order them. Where had he been before he went to sleep. What had he dreamed.

What arose was Sheath's white throat, the black slash of her hair. This as if seen through water, as if she lay beneath the surface of a stream, ripples passing over her face. And wrapped in hides, his hips warmed, his erection growing like a worm underground. His hands went from numb to engorged with blood and stabbing feeling. Her lips and tongue shining with blood, the thick liquid running down her chin. The spectre of her fingertips pressing his thumping jugular vein.

*

When they thought he was asleep, he heard his parents speaking in hoarse whispers.

'He was too young,' his father said. 'The old man knew that. He should never have sent him.'

'But his talent …' his mother said.

'Still a boy. He should have stayed a hunter. You see how he is now. It's too big for him. He can't hold it.'

'Oh, my boy, he has taken my boy.'

[42]

*

It was near the solstice that the old man called him again. Just him, no one else. Snow lay frozen in dirty scalloped ridges along the paths and up against the walls of the houses. Clouds bloodied by the sunset. Down the long path to the sweat hut, steam from the door as breath from a mouth. He knelt and put his face to the snow and crawled in.

'Close the door,' the old man said.

Harpen found the curved piece of wood and fit it into the doorway. Slowly the red stone glow grew out of the shadows. The old man's hand passed over, and the herbs flared like yellow stars.

'Come here.'

Harpen crawled forward, feeling the damp pine needles on his palms, smelling the acrid smoke of the herbs. He sat across the stones from the old man, whose face was a red mask upon the dark.

'Your parents say you're sick.'

Harpen looked at the stones and said nothing, the wet maddening dripping over the hard pit inside.

'You don't speak to them. Will you speak to me?'

'I can speak to you.'

'You have to be honest.'

'I don't lie.'

'All right.'

The old man spread more herbs on the rocks and smoke slithered over the blood glow.

'Tell me your dreams.'

A feeling wormed over Harpen's skin, his lips would not stay still.

'I don't dream.'

'Everyone dreams, be honest.'

'I don't sleep, I try to keep awake.'

'Why.'

'I see things. Not dreams. They are real things. So I don't close my eyes.'

[43]

The old man was quiet for a long time.

'You see the killing,' he said at last.

The spear standing black and slick, trailing its burning flag, and not falling, not falling, always. And in the blood light of the coals, the eyes staring and staring and sliding down but still watching.

'I always see it,' Harpen said. His lungs wet and cavernous. 'Always. I don't want it there, I don't want to see it,' he said.

The old man was very still for a long time. The glow of the stones diminishing, the tiny stars of the herbs going out.

'Boy,' said the old man. 'I am sorry. I tell you I am sorry down through my metal for what you have had to do.'

He breathed in, deep and whistling as a gust through the crags.

'And I cannot take it back now. A killer must live with what he has seen and done. There is nothing now but to live and be grateful for what you have.'

All italicised language is quoted from the poetry of Robinson Jeffers. This is an excerpt from a novel in progress, Seek a Minor Sun

Armadillo

Kim Goldberg

Once there were two brothers who lived on the back of an armadillo. The armadillo was so large and slow-moving that the two brothers, along with everyone else aboard the lumbering beast, assumed it was a planet.

As children, the two brothers were great inventors. When they were ten, they made a waterwheel from their mother's teaspoons. The family stirred its tea with butter knives after that. The waterwheel powered a small defibrillator the brothers had built from an electric shaver. Their father grew a beard after that. The brothers searched high and low and in every corner of their yard, and even the neighbour's yard, looking for something to defibrillate. But they could find nothing fibrillating. This was a setback to their research. They put their homemade defibrillator and waterwheel away.

When the brothers grew up, their careers took them to opposite ends of the armadillo (which they still took to be a planet). One brother inserted sonic probes deep into the creature to record the ultra low-frequency rumblings. These rumblings were actually the armadillo's heart beating. The other brother constructed an enormous saucer-shaped ear and pointed it heavenward to record the faint strands of star chatter hidden among space noise. These chattering songs were, in fact, mating vocalisations of amorous armadillos a great distance away.

[45]

The brothers, being full-fledged scientists by now, knew all about beat frequencies: the sonic outcome when one frequency is laid atop another. And so they combined their recordings of inner and outer space to see what would happen. The resulting pulse triggered ancient neural pathways, flooding the two brothers with a cascade of endorphins and euphoria (to say nothing of its effect on the armadillo). It was at this point that the corporate sector took an interest in the brothers' research.

Amplifiers were erected across the land so the beats would reach the entire population. Soon people were standing in line all night to purchase the latest release of neck-collar receivers. A free pad of post-it notes accompanied each receiver since quite a lot was being forgotten by now. (Hypomnesia turned out to be an unanticipated consequence of the addiction to beats.)

Things could have gone on this way indefinitely, or at least until all available surfaces were filled with post-it notes. However, the armadillo began to fibrillate. Cans fell from shelves. Fruit fell from trees. Birds fell from perches. Committees were struck to assess the Falling Crisis. Emergency Response Teams were deployed to all corners of the armadillo, although most forgot their mission and wandered aimlessly from town to town, opening pop-up road-kill cafés and sleeping in barns.

The two brothers managed to revive each other from their euphoric drift. They sensed they bore some responsibility for the current predicament. They vaguely recalled something about a defibrillator. The brothers returned to their childhood home where they searched high and low and in every corner of their yard, and even the neighbour's yard, looking for something they dimly remembered building many years ago. But the longer they searched, the hazier

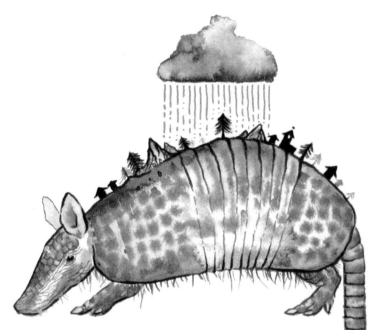

their compromised memories grew until they thought they were looking for a Christmas fruitcake.

Their parents, who no longer recalled they had two sons, believed the brothers were workmen come to replace the roof tiles. After a few hours, the elderly couple offered the workmen tea with butter knives. Eventually, the armadillo expired and the falling stopped.

This story is also available as an audio version read by the author.
See page 241 for more details, or visit dark-mountain.net/issue-18-fabula-audio

Illustrations by **Bethan McFadden**

Tell Me What You See

Ekow Manuar

The Fields

'Tell me what you see, Mavis?' Tawiah asked through Mavis's earpiece as she stood at the hilled boundary of the forty-acre green pepper farm. Mavis tuned her i-specs, adjusting the crops from cabbage to green pepper, and instantly saw a set of new characteristics pop up on her augmented vision. The i-specs picked up the general atmospheric conditions, then the state of the crops, and finally the three farmers working on the fields. The weather was good, thirty-two degrees, a big drop from the average temperatures due to the intense cloud cover. Humidity was also favourable. However, the peppers were dehydrated. The heat of the last few days had been intense, and the i-specs could tell that significant application of water was needed to deter any deformations to the crops as they advanced through this crucial stage of their growth. She tuned the i-specs to tell her the weather forecast for the next few days and any sort of precipitation did not seem likely.

'The crops are dry, and in need of water. Rain is not looking so likely. We would have to turn on the irrigation system,' Mavis said to Tawiah, who was sitting halfway across the country in the Ministry of Food and Agriculture offices in New Accra.

'Let me just do a cross check with Drone H32. Oh, wait...Daryl is on his way with it as we speak,' Tawiah's high-pitched voice said through the earpiece. 'He will be there in twenty minutes, so you can relax till then.'

Mavis decided to slump down the hill toward the farmers, hoping

[48]

to get a kernel of boiled corn to chew on. From the top of the hill she made her way through the rows of peppers, planted on small beds, all the way down to the tank tower, under which the farmers were taking a break from their early morning labour. She always loved coming to the countryside. There was a peace here that was hardly available to her in New Accra, where life bustled at a robust pace.

The countryside was something else though. The uninterrupted expanse of green stretching over the rolling hills in the southern end of the Eastern Region. An endearing sight of human geometry. The fixed plots, square shapes, and shades of green acted as a patchwork and were easy on the eye. In New Accra, the eye always seemed to be distracted by some unnecessary visual litter, each distraction feeding into a string of thoughts that only induced anxieties in Mavis. It was all too much in the city, and being out here was in its way cleansing for her eyes, mind and heart.

Thinking about her eyes, Mavis removed the i-specs as she approached the farmers, Emmanuel, Attah and Sampson. Mavis always found them a little distant from her, and having the glasses on didn't help in breaching that gap.

She engaged them in some light banter. They made some comments about the drones doing all their work, then they gave her a kernel of corn to share with them. All was good, good enough at least.

After she was done she walked over to the little farmhouse and went to the tank's faucet and turned the tap over and let the cool water run over her hands, dripping down into the damp earth. The pressure was a little low, and she had the urge to check the water level with her i-specs, but thought it unsavoury to so openly show distrust to the farmers. Instead, she shook her hands before flopping down onto a wooden bench in front of the farmhouse, waiting for Daryl to fly over.

Sleep came easily enough but was shortly disrupted by Emmanuel, who poked Mavis awake, pointing to the distant skies. Mavis collected herself, and heard the faint chopping of drone wings. There was a black figure with dangling legs emerging from the clouds. The image slowly enlarged as it made its way towards Mavis. She could vaguely make out Daryl smoking something, most likely weed, as he began his descent. The clouded sky temporarily parted to let the sun's rays shine through.

The chopping sounds from the drone had smoothed out and she heard Daryl shout a greeting to the farmers before he was standing in front of Mavis, hands in pockets, a lit joint between his blackened lips.

'Mavis, you dey?' His voice deep and rasp.

'I dey, Daryl. Where are you coming from?'

'Begoro, but had to make some stops and supervise the drone spraying over some of the fields that are about to harvest. The green peppers have been struggling. So HQ said we should spray some more fertiliser to sort them – now. As you know, gotta fulfil quota!'

Mavis couldn't help but laugh at Daryl's use of the word 'now'. Daryl was anything but a typical Nigerian, but that word popped up at the most oddest of times, and it just negated everything Daryl projected of himself.

'I see that you are laughing at me again.'

'You, don't worry. Finish smoking your weed, then we will do what we have to do here.'

'Yo! Aunty.'

Mavis was always comfortable with Daryl. On her field duties, he was the closest thing to home she had. Daryl had been part of the Greater Ghana Alliance (GGA), the current governing party of Ghana, and the Netherlands Enterprise Agency's (RVO's) joint agriculture programme since it was started five years ago. It was a simple partnership: RVO would bring in technical and capital support, and the GGA would ensure that a huge slice of the harvest was sent to

Europe at a reduced cost. Win-win, they said. Mavis didn't make much of it, and Daryl didn't let on much of his thoughts on it either, just that he had done a similar programme in Nigeria and was almost killed for it. Other than that, she actually didn't know so much about Daryl. If he had a family, a wife, a home. Actually, Mavis would abuse Daryl's silence by loading him with her own life problems. He didn't offer much in advice, but his grunts of acceptance or dismay were very welcome to Mavis.

The sun was about climbing to midday and the clouds were all but gone when Mavis and Daryl got up to activate the drone for its field tests. By this time, the farmers had made their way to the town of Petro to look for a decent meal. Mavis felt more comfortable bringing up her earlier concerns.

'The crops are dry, above and below ground. But the farmers said they watered it, and HQ confirmed this as well.'

'Eh?'

'I think there might be something off, maybe the farmers can tell us when they are back?'

'Mhm. There could be many things off. Let us take it one step at a time for now.' Daryl launched into a rapid stride, heading to the top of the hill Mavis had previously been on. As Daryl placed the earpiece carefully in the nook of his ear and confirmed his position, Mavis took notice of his shortened forefinger. Daryl had said he lost it when he was in Nigeria working for the programme there. The farmers had revolted violently, and he had been caught up in the middle of it. Mavis wondered what set of circumstances would lead to such violence?

Now, as much as ever, she yearned to see her family again, even her nagging parents. Being close to all of them was home for her. Presently, home was many thousand miles away. All she had was Daryl, the Drone H32, and her pair of i-specs.

Pressures

Mavis and Daryl were both synced to HQ, with Tawiah quickly disbursing instructions to Daryl on what configurations to set on the Drone H32, before setting it off to run its tests over the fields. HQ wasn't only home to the Ministry of Food and Agriculture, there was also a large RVO contingency in the building. They had technical staff manning laptops that were connected to all their remote agric-programmes across the sub-region.

The GGA had done a lot of work in their time in office. Their mantra of 'economic empowerment' permeated every single branch of government, down to the secretaries. It wasn't just a saying, or a great plan shelved in some report, as with incumbent governments of before. When the GGA said something, they meant it.

For the Ministry of Food and Agriculture, the policy directives were primarily to export high-value crops to bolster the national purse and develop the agricultural sector. Underlying that directive were soft expansionist policies intended to pump Ghanaian produce and commodities into Francophone Africa. Ghanaian agri-businesses were given huge support and leeway to operate their businesses if they were outward-facing. Over five years, Ghanaian companies were out-competing their francophone counterparts, and soon consuming their businesses.

The flip side was the GGA's dealing with China. Once the GGA had sufficient leverage to pull across West Africa, it became easier to entice Chinese mega-infrastructure projects. With the GGA as the focal point, the bureaucracies of transacting such mega-projects would largely reduce.

It had taken on a magnificent shape, and it was now a matter of keeping the clockwork ticking. And that was the problem of having huge harvests lost in the Ghanaian countryside. If the GGA failed to deliver on their end of the bargain, then that would leave them in a vulnerable position at the negotiating table.

Of course, Daryl and Tawiah were extremely privy to these stakes, but to Mavis it was something of a distant concern. The only way it impacted her was how much work she had to do. If she had to visit one less site, she was better for it. If she had more sites, ah well! The job was just a means to take care of her family.

As she leaned over Daryl, who had been kneeling down over the drone, wiping sweat dripping from his temple, she took notice of the crops. It wasn't the first time that she found herself paying particular attention to their well-being. Her hand fluttered over her tummy as she made to crouch and observe the deformities in the fruit, the green peppers in this case. Some of them had healthy well-rounded peppers with a rich glossy green on them. The vast majority, though, were struggling to keep colour, their shapes crumpling. She couldn't help but make the comparisons to her own offspring. That is what they were at the end of the day, the peppers, her kids, they were offspring. And for one reason or the other, their parents had failed to provide all that was necessary for them to survive.

'I am done, Mavis. Let's get started before the boys come back to the farm.'

Mavis sighed to herself for getting so worked up worrying about offspring.

'Why are you concerned about them?' she said, referring to the farmers.

Daryl didn't respond, his eyes fixed on the remote as he steered the drone upward and alerted Tawiah that all systems were good to go.

'Yes, we are clear. Will run hydrological assessments,' Mavis and Daryl both heard through the earpiece.

Then the drone was off. In the course of its ascent, its wings grew larger and Mavis could see a number of sensors revealing themselves on the underside of its wings. Blue orbs, shining, then casting waves of light over the grounds as it scoped the fields.

'So the crops have been lacking water, but from our reports we have seen that the irrigation system has been in use. So, how?' Tawiah mumbled to himself over the communication.

The drone was now hovering over the water tank, then it shifted over the borehole, at which point it lowered itself.

'Checking borehole levels. I am just getting reports from the technical team here, that there has been a region-wide reduction in water tables. And it looks like our borehole is...is...wow...it is virtually empty. Low replenishing rates too.'

'Impossible.' Daryl shook his head.

'I am going to assess the other five boreholes in the area. Wow – wow. This is not good.' Mavis could hear Tawiah whizzing through dozens of screens miles away in his office.

Daryl had placed the control pad for the drone down on the ground, as he wiped more sweat with his shirt. He then pressed his earpiece two times to open communication with the technical team at HQ.

'Guys, can you hear me?'

'Loud and clear, Daryl,' Mavis heard.

'We are in a bit of a situation down here. These fields represent about twenty percent of the vegetable produce. The crops can be saved,' Daryl was pacing his words, Mavis realised. A strategy he adopted every so often to give himself more time. 'I need to talk to the farmers.'

'Hi Daryl, this is Folkert. What the fuck do you mean you need to talk to the farmers?! What the fuck does that mean, ay?!' Mavis had only heard Folkert's voice once, and it had been to lay insult upon insult on her during one of her first-ever field trips. He was the programme supervisor for RVO, and it was safe to say that when you heard his Dutch accent, it wasn't a good thing.

'We need to gather information, even your own organisation's manual on dealing with crisis—'

'Don't give me that bullshit! We have a *quota* from you...'

'Absolutely, so let me handle it.' Daryl disconnected his earpiece and quickly gestured for Mavis to do the same.

'We don't have time.' He was taking long strides down the hill, a sudden urgency.

'What are you talking about?' Mavis was following behind, her heart pounding in her chest now.

'Can't you tell what has happened here? Have you been to any villages or towns of late?' They were back down in the farmhouse and Daryl was scrambling around looking for something.

'No, I haven't. After the site visits I am taken straight back to the lodge.' Mavis wasn't able to keep up with Daryl who was still scrummaging around, tossing papers and furniture about.

'Where are the car keys?!'

'What? There is no car here. The batteries needed to be replaced. Haven't gotten it back...'

'Fuck-shit!'

'Daryl! Can you please tell me what is going on?' Mavis had grabbed Daryl by the arm and was yelling right into his face. The fervour that had taken over him still coursing through his body.

'I saw this happen in Nigeria, when I was near Kano. It is water. Our operations must have sucked the land dry of water. And since we don't live here, we wouldn't know if the people have been suffering as well – now. The farmers must have taken the water out and moved it to their villages to supply their people.'

'OK, but why...'

'These people we are dealing with, the GGA or RVO, Folkert, or whoever. The money involved... What do you think they will do if they find out these farmers are stealing their water?' Daryl had moved out of the farmhouse, heading back to the hill they had been scoping from.

'Do you think that they will actually use force?' Mavis was feeling the heat of the sun pressing on her.

'You think the farmers were the ones who cut off my finger?'

After a moment's pause, Mavis had to catch up with Daryl who was now climbing the hill again.

[55]

'So what are we going to do?' She didn't know what made her add the word 'we' to the sentence. It could easily have been 'you', just Daryl, but for whatever reason, she was now very much involved.

'We have to get to the farmers, quick! Get them to understand the consequences. Get them to agree to use the water to irrigate the crops, assure them that we will provide water. Then communicate with HQ.'

'Why quickly?'

'Folkert has probably used time-lapse aerial satellite images to show what happened to the water – they will know. They will deploy.'

'But how will we get there before them?'

Daryl had his hand over his eyes, shielding them from the sun, which was lashing a blinding sheen upon them. After a second or two, he pointed to the heavens and answered Mavis.

'With that.'

Wings

Daryl had managed to unscrew the control pad to override HQ's control over H32. Mavis stood in awe as she watched Daryl struggle to redirect the drone towards the hill where they were standing, then down to a height at which they could mount the airborne machine. Drone H32 was built for bulk transportation of agriculture goods, as well as the odd human. But not two. Daryl handed the pad to Mavis to hold as he lifted himself onto the hanging seat, then beckoned Mavis to follow suit. She tossed the device over, but as she was preparing to launch herself towards Daryl's waiting hands, she had a moment's hesitation.

Why did she need to get involved? This was all Daryl's doing, right? He had flung her into this conflict between the farmers and the GGA. In fact, it was in her best interest to stay put, and see it out from the safe haven of the farmhouse. Keeping her job, her income, and her family back in New Accra well fed and catered for.

Daryl's arms had been flexed for a while, but now they were beginning to dangle like loose strings of noodles.

'Mavis?!' he yelled over the chopping sound of the drone blades.

'Why should I follow you?' she asked plainly.

Daryl paused a second. Then acceptance of this moment's doubt on Mavis's part spread over him like a breath.

'You don't have to do anything, Mavis…'

Without really knowing why, Mavis sighed and tossed her hands up to Daryl who instantly tensed himself to lift her up onto the drone. Once she was on top of his lap, he rubbed her leg and she scowled in return, before eventually smiling too.

'Oga, I hope you can fly this thing!'

'Don't worry – now!'

The ride was bumpy at first. Getting the ascent right without jerking violently from side to side was difficult for Daryl. But once at a good elevation, it became as easy as simply pointing the joy-stick in the right direction. With the drone stabilised, as well as Mavis's heart propulsions, she could let her eyes wander over the rustic beauty of the low-lying hills of the Eastern Region. She always had a great vantage point on top of the hill at the green pepper farm, overlooking the valley. But now the patchwork was below her feet. The subtle variations in green. The wide landscape, stretching on to the horizon. The patches of forests standing tall between the rolling hills. The vast tracts of land excavated for development.

Development, in this case, meaning the pursuit of foreign currency through the export of high-value crops, on land that, Mavis reminded herself, had once belonged to farmers, chiefs, or shared through families. Land that would be used as collateral to form so-called 'partnerships' between the GGA and the farmers, with the aim of increasing yield and income. But from what Mavis had been increasingly gathering, actually contributing to the farmers' indentureship to the GGA. Win-win, was how it was heralded. But win-win was hardly the case. The farms didn't produce incredibly high yields and the farmers' incomes did not surpass their expenses. Finally, loan payments weren't met on time and soon, the land signed as collateral was being handed over to the GGA. But all the time Mavis witnessed this, she consoled herself with the fact that the farmers were still permitted to work on the farm and earn an income at the very least.

There was no denying that the beauty she saw in the landscape a moment ago was now tainted by her developing realisation. Beyond the neat lines, fences, and promises of new hybrid seeds and other agric-technologies, there was a silent war going on.

Mavis looked over at Daryl, who had been pensive since they were stable.

'Daryl, was what happened in Nigeria … the reason you left?' she asked.

Daryl remained as he was, hands wrapped on the pole connecting their seats to the main body of the H32. Then he took a deep breath and started.

'… You tell yourself that it was your job to be one way. To work and do what you are told. And you think that that will bring you fulfilment. You see, now. Like the way you feel when you take care of your family. I did my job very well. And in Nigeria, when it came to a matter of life and death, it was death. And I didn't even know that this was the decision before me. And all the fulfilment I had felt, was gone. And I just thought of what I would do if I got the chance again …'

They sat in silence as the first thatched roofs began to show themselves below their feet. Mavis could see scores of children making their way from a compound with buckets on top of their heads.

'You know which chop-bar the farmers go?' Mavis asked.

'Most likely, they didn't even go and eat …'

'Ahh, OK.'

'We need to go to the chief's house. You have met him before?'

'Not the new one, but his compound is where the children were coming from.'

'Then let me land in the football field.'

Mavis held onto the handlebars placed on either side. The chopper's change of direction caused the air to cut to a different sound, and she felt her tummy lift up unpleasantly as they dropped down.

Us or Them

Mavis sat beside Daryl on two bended plastic chairs, with Attah and Emmanuel leaning behind them on a low-lying wall of the veranda. Large chunks of the house remained unpainted and Mavis could make out the fashioned lines for electrical wiring. The compound itself was vast. The veranda they were in was not the chief's, but rather, that of one of the elders: Mr. Richard, Attah had referred to him as. There were no children in sight, as Mavis nervously did some more scoping of the compound, waiting for Mr. Richard to attend to them.

Once it was plain that there would be no distractions for Mavis to mindlessly consider, she settled on Daryl who had sat still, concentrated on the floor.

Finally, the one called Mr. Richard made his way through the beaded entry of the house. He was wearing a holed shirt, and had wrapped a cloth around his protruding stomach. He didn't look much, but Mavis knew that out here in the countryside, things weren't ever as they seemed.

Daryl and Mavis had decided that she would talk to the elder because Nigerians weren't seen so kindly in these parts.

'Mr. Richard, we are sorry to disturb your evening,' Mavis filled in after an awkward silence.

'My evenings of late have been more troubling. But what can we do?' he replied stiffly.

'I hear you senior,' she looked at Daryl, and his eyes egged her on.

'It is unfortunate that we come to you with no arrangements to meet. But sometimes, such meetings are forced onto us.'

'We do not have control over God's will... So what can I do for you?' Mr. Richard asked.

This was the point at which she had hoped Daryl could jump in. But it was upon Mavis to explain the developing situation, and let Mr. Richard know the possible implications for his village. The way she would word it was of the utmost importance. One false move, let's say, subtly accusing the elders of wrongdoing, would cause the whole intervention to collapse.

'Let me start by saying that I am sorry that I have not come to introduce myself formally. I am Mavis Obeng, and I work at the Ministry of Food and Agriculture. I have been working alongside Attah and Emmanuel for the last year, on their farms…'

Mr. Richard wasn't looking at them. His gaze was set on a space over Mavis and Daryl, in the corner of the veranda's ceiling.

'As of now, our situation is very some-way. The government *obronis* know about the water,' Mavis explained. Mr. Richard's eyes pulled down to hers. A retort building in his stomach. But before he could blurt it out, Mavis intervened.

'We know that you have had no choice. We aren't here to attack you…' And with that Mr. Richard's expanding stomach released.

Assured that she could continue, Mavis persisted.

'But we need you to know that, these people do not reason like us. They will see this as an insult. They are coming…' Mavis said, but felt like its impact was lost on Mr. Richard, who stared blankly. Daryl, again, urged her to continue.

'These are not government officials, oh!' Mavis said, then glanced at Daryl, who nodded encouragingly. 'These are soldiers, armed with guns. Soldiers who don't know right or wrong, and know no allegiance but to money. You understand, Mr. Richard? Men without nationalities, or tribes, or even families. Men who know no such thing as mercy, for you, for me, the younglings…just money,' Mavis ended softly, Daryl beaming at her with what looked like pride.

Mr. Richard, who had looked likely to boil over at every other word Mavis had said, seemed to have reconsidered his assumption about her and Daryl. He readjusted the wrap around his waist before speaking.

'I know you, madam Mavis. I remember when you first came,' he was back staring at the space above Mavis's head. 'Our situation, as you said, is a difficult one. I have known that at all times, water has been available to Petro. And never in my sixty-seven good years living here have I encountered such a drastic situation. I must say that this has coincided with the government programme. But alas, our world offers no justice for the feeble. So we must make it for ourselves.'

'The justice you think you are making, I am afraid to say, will only cause a bigger injustice on yourself,' Mavis said flatly, and thinking that she had finally crossed the line, waited with bated breath to see Mr. Richard's response.

Mr. Richard withdrew a little, his nostrils expanding ever so slightly then contracting again.

'So, what do you think we should do?' Mr. Richard said solemnly.

Mavis didn't have a clue. What could they do? Say they are sorry and then give the water back?

Mavis was running through all the possible solutions her imagination could conjure up. When she had burned through all of them (they weren't many), she looked up at Mr. Richard, a clueless expression on her face, then at Daryl, who seemed ready to burst. Mavis nodded her head at him to say something, and he was about to, when Emmanuel cut in.

'Bosso Richard, I de hear some che-che-che.'

They all quietened, straining their ears to hear what Emmanuel was talking about. Then, Mavis heard it. The faint but unmistakable chopping sound of not one, but many drones.

This is an excerpt from 'Tell Me What You See', a long short story set in mid-21st-century Ghana

Asphodels and Infidels

Lynsey Wright

The asphodels rose prickly out of the earth: a small cluster huddled conspiratorially. Their long stems waving high above the ground gracefully, lording themselves above everything but the sky. On the ground a metallic beetle froze underneath their long-cast shadows, continuing on only when the wind blew and shifted their positions enough to provide nurturing shafts of sunlight again. As the wind picked up both beetle and plants looked as if locked in a complex ancient dance, a ritualistic expression that existed before words began to express concrete needs, both vying to communicate a lesson, or a thought, or a feeling previously unexpressed.

The boot came down, casting a deep shadow, a disturbance in the air, and crushed both the delicate stems of the flowers and the beetle. The man trudged along the cliff's edge, looking out towards the empty horizon, devoid of ships, land or any signs of life. He understood how people could think this watery perimeter was the very end of the Earth; as if anything that dared pass that far out from land would be swallowed down whole, clean off the edge, deep into the centre of the Earth or out into a vacuum of space.

He meandered, sometimes following the vague paths that were carved out of parted and flattened grass, other times he forged his own way through unsullied stems of wild blooms and bountiful weed clusters. He wondered at intervals if he was the first person to ever tread on this particular patch of earth. He liked to imagine the untouched places; the silent plateau of a distant high mountain; the dank depths of an inaccessible cave; the rugged raw face of a seaside cliff; the treacherous inner rim of an active volcano spewing noxious gases; all virgin land, unknown to mankind, undefiled by human touch. He had begun to understand the symbiotic nature of the planet, the human impact so costly to so precarious a balancing act, but humans were 'nature' too, and this thought calmed him.

He led what he would call a 'simple life'; he was free of the trappings he had observed in other folk: didn't drink, or go out much, preferred acquaintances instead of friends, and bore life as a dutiful responsibility rather than an alluring opportunity. He didn't reach for the things that existed outside of his means, seemed content to stay within his four walls, woke early and ate blandly. He wondered about the vastness of the oceans, the high places, the out of reach places but not with a desire to reach them or to know them, but as a comfort that they merely existed and weren't dependent on humankind nor in fact knew anything of it – they oftentimes were here long before and would be here long afterwards.

His house stood apart, on a grassy knoll before a steep verge that led down to a private beach that was reserved for mating seabirds. His job was as caretaker to these rare birds, ensuring no tourists attempted the dangerous climb down to disturb their nesting. Few tried, but he was unable to rescue one photographer who had lost her footing and broken her neck. The helicopter sent to retrieve her body was unable to reach the secluded spot. For days he noted the tides and charted her position, her clothes snagged on a rock which held her in place and made it seem as though she were somehow still clinging to life, until a particularly rough and windy day created huge swells that dislodged her limp and lifeless body. He watched her float away bobbing up and down in the fiery waves.

In the few days her body was present below he imagined a life with her; inviting her over for tea in the beginning, sharing his binoculars with her, pointing out Ursa Minor and other constellations he knew, showing her his favourites of the birds he had charge over, and eventually building the hearth fire as she chopped onions and wiped at her eyes with her apron, eating in silence, tuning into the radio as she picked over a puzzle.

He imagined jumping down from the lip of the cliff to join her on her sandy bed, surrounded by seaweeds of differing shapes and colours; the black ones stringy and slimy; the pale green bulbous and emphatic; the dark green casting its salt-tinged fervid scent up and across the cliff, it often woke him as it clung to his nostrils, hiding in every nook and crevice.

The days before she was swept away were tormented days. On the third day he cursed and held his hand over the boiling teapot, the skin blistered and scorched underneath. On the fourth he plunged the same hand into a pail of sea water he had collected further down the coast that he kept molluscs and crabs in – the pain from the salt in the wound searing up to his elbow. The melodious clicks and trills of the birds, that usually provided comfort to him, now grated to such an extent he aimed his shotgun into the sky and fired, clipping the wing of a juvenile who had just learned to wheel and coast on the wind. It spiralled to the ground, its feathers akimbo.

After she had gone, his peace was restored. He bandaged up his hand, put away his binoculars and sat down to eat his first full meal in days; a foil-wrapped potato which he carefully dredged out of the back of the stove with fire-proof metal tongs.

His life moved on, as before. Still she floated further out to sea, towards the unknown place that lay beyond the edge of the luminous horizon.

Fiona Banner aka The Vanity Press
Bank Gothic (close), Oil on found painting, 2019
All images © Fiona Banner aka The Vanity Press

Fiona Banner aka The Vanity Press
New York, Roemisch Liegend, Modern, Collegiate, Diptych, Oil on found painting, 2019
All images © Fiona Banner aka The Vanity Press

Sarah Ainslie
Bridging Rainham's Past, Photomontage, 2019

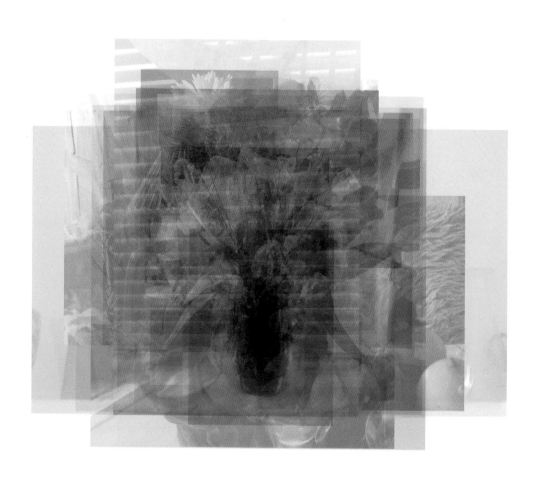

William Bock and Lena Spindler
[above] *All your flower photographs*, Giclée print, 2017
[opposite] *Eighteen years, one view*, Giclée print, 2017

The Still Life series is a body of work that emerged while the artist mourned his mother's death. Digitally layering his mother's archive of photographs she took over many years, Bock created new composite images each representing months or even years spent noticing the ebb and flow of life in plants and the landscape.

Luisa-Maria MacCormack
Pan in the Bushes,
Pastel on paper, 2019

The Ecstatic Climate Change Porn Machine

Kathryn Kuitenbrouwer

As we were fucking, I noticed a tiny black spider entering a hole in the wallboard ceiling and it made me laugh. Later, after the other guy left and Hank arrived home from work, we watched the dog circling his tail for a minute, and then another minute and then, miraculously, another one, his tail sprung with doggish desperation to mouth it. When he finally succeeded, Hank muttered, 'Ouroboros,' and I pretended not to understand because it was at that stage in our marriage that I enjoyed the feeling of finding him insufferable, and this was one way I orchestrated this feeling, by goading him into lengthy mansplainations about arcane mythology. I would nod and think, while he droned on, about having sex with the other guy while spiders built their homes in the roof pitch.

The interactions with Hank had become so samey – one time to the next – that I barely registered them. My Hankish orgasms were as morning tea: pleasant, necessary, but barely caffeinated. It was as much as in life, as soon as you noticed something, like really made note, you began to see it everywhere. The roof pitch beadboard gap, by way of example. Because where was that wolf spider heading with such diligent intention? That spider had me thinking about portals. Ways out.

Later that night, the night after the spider sighting, I took my cellphone flashlight and then my Maglite and peered into the hole. I saw nothing but a wisp of Tyvek and the taupe of ancient mildewy beaverboard, some pink fluff. Half despairingly, half resignedly I jumped off the bed, flipped the flashlights off, and then the bedroom switch too, and was about to fully abandon even the lingering image of a spider glancing over its shoulder as it tucked into the roof's abyss, when a glint of grass green evanesced at me from the gap. Naturally, I furrowed my brow, climbed back on the bed, peered back into – nothing – just a cloud of insulation. My fervent imagination, I thought, and – goodnight, spider.

Folks put great stock in love, and I am one of them. I pursue it everywhere. In the heart of a wee wolf spider heading home, in the other guy, in Hank (and especially his skivvy choices, about which more later). It was not always thus; my heart was once encased and locked as much as the next person. But then, some two years ago, I participated in an ayahuasca *cura* of botany and chant from which I emerged three thousand, seven hundred and ninety-three times remedied. It's impossible to articulate this to most people but *you* get it. Most people reckon out of only one hundred but you (and I) know better. In that ceremony, I did not see the fractals of the fractals of the fractals so much as I knew them. They hunkered without and within me. I spent the night prying my ribcage open in order to let more of it in, to let it all in. The outcome of this now long-ago experience, as you well know, has been profound. I won't distress you with the details again, the shocking biological alterations, the shivering sudden flutter and then wild riving of my heart chakra.

I did just now hesitate to use the term chakra since I know it troubles some, pegs me as a lunatic, or else an American – the enlightened sort. I do not wish to alienate the already alienated. Let the pink rush into you as liquid marvel and let it race about.

Like I said, words fail.

The other guy: I met them on Tinder. It began as a thought experiment and ended in a roadside motor inn, a streak of their mess across the sheets while their muted conference call babbled on in the background about subclauses and actionables. El dorado. Egress. I did not know myself. It would be a lie to say it ended there. It continues on into this day still. Hence, the miracle of the spider sighting in the marital bed. I like to think that if you can let even a spider into your rigorous sexual relation, then if that is not love, love is bunk. I was just and always following the trail. What marriage cannot withstand a little bliss?

Note: there is joy in mockery. It is not the holiest of joys but harmless. Do no harm, manifest no injury! My baiting Hank is just such harmlessness. One, he likes it, gets off on it even. Two, he angles for it the way a cat presents its asshole. Three, we make space for this just as a blanket provides comforting weight. There are myriad ways of loving and this is one. We wrap ourselves in this marital ritual and find something there. Ask him if you like. He tells me he finds it cheeky, sexy even.

The glint of green reminded me of something. Some far away something that was never meant for me until that moment I saw it again. I tried to forget it, to leave it alone for the spider and her kin but it crept and flashed at me now and again in that strange space between waking and sleeping when the brain comes to know all things. I even thought that I was going insane. But it came back fleetingly in other moments of intense languidity, too: in the calm before orgasm, the second or two after a first sip of coffee, the clarity of vision after a rigorous jog. That green was unmistakable. The next time with the other guy, after disrobing them of their motorcycle leathers and after I caught their flaccid sex in between my teeth and they arced into it and hardened, I saw it again.

'Green,' I said, 'I see colours,' which was not exactly new.

'Green.' They pulled away and squeezed themselves in a way that looked as if they were closing a ketchup cap over and over again. 'Grass green, right?'

And I had to admit that, yes.

'The colour of grass and leaves in the earliest manifestation of life in springtime,' they added, and gave a wee frown in the direction of their member.

'How?' I asked, because how could they know?

And they, horny, smiled and told me that I shouldn't worry and then they leant over me and performed a small benediction on the new tattoo I had just acquired. 'Thank you,' I said. And then, 'There is something beyond me, interstitial...'

'... in the layer that expands into infinity, yeah, I know,' and they nudged my mouth back over their now flaccid-again thing.

There is nothing I enjoy more than the feeling of the other guy growing tumescent in my mouth. That sense of being filled. That power to bite or not. A grand thank you right now to all the glorious energy of the universe for the nothing that becomes something.

'You OK?' the other guy said.

I gestured with my eyes that I was.

'I'm going to come,' they said.

And so I stopped and said, 'No, you fucking well are not going to come. You are going to hold that thought.'

The other guy nodded with a solemnity one generally finds only in altar boys and girls circa 1960, an era now lost to irony and fretfulness and video gaming. I wished I had a handful of holy hosts to feed them in that moment. I wished I could remember the words to the Lord's Prayer but instead I hummed it and they watched their glorious member hold itself in suspension, while I occasionally licked its tip by way of encouragement.

By comparison, my relationship with Hank had become an exchange economy – I do not recall when this happened to us. In our sex act there was nothing but the tawdry remnants of capitalism playing out as tit for tat. And so I had come to seek joy in the comedy of his underpants, which was all he dared by way of self-expression. The hidden delight of three hundred dollar undies he would shard up by day's end. He preferred wild patterns of robots and sneakers, effigies of extinct animals, and for the sake of all the saints, I loved him for this. This private scatology. And it was, along with the mockery, enough to keep me in his orbit. Or enough of his orbit that it was still marriage. That sort of love was still love. I let it hope for nothing, tried to let it tell its own story, let it vibrate at its own distinct frequency, however unremarkable to the rest of you.

Let this heart beat in my closed fist.

The other guy had their palm now on the outer clit that climbed around my vaginal tract – in that spot just above my pubis and was rubbing there while their other hand plunged heaven into me. I felt only gratitude rising in me until I caught sight, in strange repetition, of the wolf spider looking both ways and deking into the roof. The other guy smiled; they're tracking my eyes, I realised. 'Yes,' they said. 'That's right,' and that's when the green flashed again and I jolted through my whole being because of what they were doing to me but also because of the colour effusing me from tip to toe.

'Do you like it?'

'Yes, I like it,' is what I would have said if there was any chance a word could come out. No word could come out. And the green became me in a new way. Synesthesia 2.0. I was gone. I do not know for how long. And where I went to I'm not sure I am at liberty to tell you. I struggle here to amply contain it in words: it's like the old Hebraic edict to not name the sacred. To speak around it by way of forming some ineffable whirl of love. But this holy was not what

[69]

you'd expect. No central unnameable. No guy in robes, his hands in supplication. It wasn't like that at all.

It was a network. The green entered and exited as a convulsion. I could hear the other guy gently laughing – a soft south-eastern breeze and they were riding this thing with me – a crest, a fall, a new crest, rolling over first me and so on, as if they were subsumed in this thing along with me, with the bed, the house, Hank, the spider, and the wolf from whencesoever it achieved its name, plus the hole in the roof pitch, all of nature, and the Morris pattern on Hank's newest underwear. A network that had no border, lines that didn't have breadth or width but rather articulated a shape that shifted even as I began to note it. It was effusively green, shades and hues that existed only in some mad Pantone innovator's fever dream. As it changed so did I and, here I came and came again.

Thank you, other guy.

There are all manner of folk in here. They scrutinise me from shy distances; they applaud the way the words collide in my mind as if they can read me as I narrate them. They can. One is little and girlish, cocking its head and nodding, but when I reach out it pulls back, aghast.

'Hello,' I venture.

It shakes its head and laughs, looks around at the others as they chatter out their green green language. It is a lexicon of leaves and organs – hearts, nerves, systems, tumbling out of them all at once, like some unfathomable communal joke. It is a chatter to which they begin to dance. It's hard to describe. But it rains their vocabulary. It torques and plumes as pollen and clouds. A green so green it is here yellow and there black and now I smell the other guy breaching into this realm. Their sweet reek repeats, 'Are you OK?' and I nod, because the creatures have come closer and I can see that there is moss growing from their eyes and there is soil caked in every rugged crevice of their faces. It makes me smile. I'm there and here. The other guy slows progress and I think that they are humming along to the discordant movement of the faery talk.

'Not faery,' the other guy says. The words come as wafts of body pong. The creatures, too, are tut-tutting, waggling inky thought and facetious root in my direction. It's impressive. And that is when the wolf spider reappears through the wee triangular gap in my heart that I had not ever before noticed. I hear it at first – an ululation of passionate mourning, a chant of gravel that splays me wide open, raw meat tending toward bacterial decay, to sink and rise as fruity toadstool, the gills of which are too sublime to be reckoned in this alphabet. Have you yet felt the spores descend upon you? Pay attention because they fall as the tiniest hum erupting along your flesh. You notice it first through the skin that circumnavigates your toes, it is as life, is it not? The other guy has located the melody and glottals me along its meaning. I taste wet earth in my mouth. I smell it all.

Is this not story?

Is this not the story into which you always wanted to be written?

Be not afraid. Plant this seed into your belly button, the divot there. An acorn, the roots anchor first and look! The folk are clapping little tongues and anuses, asterisk-like puckered mouths, a hieroglyphic of joyous appetite and it occurs to me before another wave of something I'll call beauty roils me in its embrace: where has the other guy gone to?

The room comes into pink focus, linen and bed and flesh, my pelvis, their nipples, a small stack of Hank's briefs folded but not yet put away on the dresser.

And the other guy is already back and 'Can you see it?' they are crying. And then I do; do you see it?

The first meaty leaves sprouting from the oak. A tree birthed out of your stomach. How pretty! Can you feel its power, the way it gives and receives? Can you feel the water it soaks up in order to smile from its branchlets? You grow beneficent. You are tree. A body, true form, right there. Reach.

Reach.

And I need a goddam hug. The folk have dipped down so that I can now hear the worm gossip and the lichen hearsay, the suck of rain back into itself. An inbreath that articulates what? Good. Goodness. I can't explain any of it. And I am trying so hard here.

The other guy curls around me like bark around a moose maple, stippled, and now I am wallpapered, treed. Who is this other guy?

'Shh,' they say. 'I'm not another guy, not an other at all. I'm your whencesoever. Grit. Stormwater, the river rising. I'm that overtaking you. The unruly crest from a passing car through a fast moving puddle. You are wet.'

'Lol,' I say. 'No shit.'

'If you want, we can remove his underpants from the vicinity,' they say.

'It would make this all more legible,' I say. 'More acceptable.'

'No,' they say. 'No, it doesn't.'

Can you feel the ache of it, I want to say, but the sap strangles the words as they rise up. I am choked with sweetness. Overtaken with the lust we call spring. The other guy urges me along. To be honest I am not even sure they are a guy. They are a nugget at the centre of my orbit. Something I created but that preceded me. 'Do you never ejaculate?' I ask, and they open their hands to show me their plasma. Green. It makes me laugh because why not?

'Is this the best you've got,' they ask, and it's a goddam joke, like the one about the fastest way to a man's heart being to chainsaw straight through his ribcage. But then the other guy gets serious and says, 'Do you know that in the spring the bark softens to let up the sap.'

'I do not know it.'

'Feel it, smell it, is there another sense that you have forgotten?'

they say. 'The one of the fine fine hum that graces your feet, the one the folk call the sense of knowing? The good sense.'

'The Good,' I say, and the whole of it burbles over me and up me until my sternum hurts with it all, then opens and opens and opens.

'The sense that has no metaphor,' the other guy and the folk are singing, and all I see are signifiers bursting their limits, words turned to air, and wind, pin cherries, lambs quarters. 'Scan the earth for better. Build your underwear from shit, search until you forget, the rain licks your mossy heart,' they sing, they blast.

Illustration by Jack Fawdry Tatham

There Was a Lady Who Had Sharks Under Her Skin

Philip Webb Gregg

There were bears there too, and tigers and wolves, and all manner of carnivorous things.

She walked around all her life, not knowing why she hurt so much. Always wondering why she was so hungry and so thirsty; always leaping at passing flames without a thought for her skin, which was worn and scarred from so many lost opportunities. And she would roar, sometimes, in the night, without knowing why. Or her mouth would suddenly be full of fangs and the taste of blood. And she would weep for the death she felt in her stomach, and kneel upon the floor. Not knowing why she hurt so much.

After many years of suffering, for no reason at all, she decided to find out what was wrong with her.

The first doctor she saw was a tired GP who looked at her strangely and said: *Lady, you are fine. There is nothing wrong with you. Go home, please. There are people dying out there.*

The second doctor was a little better. He at least smiled, and said she wasn't alone. And would she like some pills?

The third doctor tried to rape her. He pressed his rubber-glove hands into her crotch and whispered that he could take the pain away if only she would put his cock in her mouth.

After that, she gave up on doctors.

Instead, she went east. And in an ashram overlooking the filthy, sacred body of the Ganges, she met a guru who claimed he could levitate using only the power of his mind. She never saw this for herself, but all the other lady yogis swore it to be true, so she thought it could be possible.

The guru agreed that yes, her chakras were out of sync, and perhaps her bandhas were a little bent, or even broken. *But these things can be fixed*, he said, smiling like a car salesman.

She left India unsatisfied, and considerably poorer than when she arrived.

On the way home she found herself stranded in Amsterdam. Flight cancelled, wallet empty, heart pounding and spitting with all the rage of all the wild creatures. So, having no destination, she walked the midnight streets, trying to warm herself and silence the roaring in her veins. It was then that she thought that perhaps the third doctor had been right, after all. Perhaps flesh was the answer.

It was winter, and the snow fell with a deadly silence in the red-lit streets, looking like blood as it congealed around the lampposts. The ladies were out in force that night. With their shining faces and false designer handbags, heavy with the scent of plastic sweetness. They grinned at her and opened their arms, and for once in her life she felt like she wasn't being lied to. Felt close to something honest. Something not yet violated by the pathetic corruption of human pretension.

So she did the only thing she could do, in the circumstances. She wedded those streets; became a bride of dark rooms and cheap perfume. Short skirt, hair bleached and wilting, lips ever smiling or snarling at those she called her prey.

She rather enjoyed it, the fucking. She had men and women of every race and class. Over and over. For years and years as the fat fell away, and her cheeks hollowed and her eyes grew sharp. And it almost, almost, worked. She could sense it, close. Something like purity. But still her toes itched to be claws and her bare breasts yearned to be smothered in fur. Still she hurt.

Then one night she met the psychopath in a coffee shop. She knew he was a psychopath, because he said so. *I feel nothing*, he said. *I am like the pale canvas drawn upon with white chalk. My emotions are like rain falling in the ocean. My self swallows all to the point where nothing survives.*

She agreed that yes, this was very interesting, and decided to take him to bed.

Later, lying starfish beside his naked body, she told him about her predicament. About her lifelong problem.

Oh, he said. *This probably won't work, but... May I?* With that he took a ballpoint pen from his bag and drew upon her ruined skin, following the pattern weaved by a thousand tiny scars. From ankle to elbow. From wrist to navel. From philtrum to anus. They looked like constellations, at first. But no, it soon became clear that what he was drawing was a zip, running all around her body. And as he traced it with the touch of the ink she felt herself unravelling, unfurling. Coming apart.

Oh fuck, she groaned, as all the wild, starving things abruptly spilled from her body, pouncing and diving and gripping the naked psychopath, who laughed as he was consumed; his last, gargled words being: *I feel... I feel...* And then there was nothing but a few scattered bones and a large pool of blood, gently seeping into the carpet.

The lady lay back, then, empty on the soiled bed, and experienced a happiness so perfect it could only be called sublime. For endless minutes she drifted through a landscape of thoughtless satisfaction. A place that fitted together absolutely. And all her walls were gone, and all her hunger filled. And her eyes shone with cleanliness and joy.

But then, suddenly, she mourned.

For Whom It Should Remain Silent

Eric Robertson

'How long has she been there?' I ask.

  'Who?'

'That woman looking at books.'

There's an old glass bookshelf running the length of the long hall-way. Floor to ceiling glass cabinet doors, framed by hundreds of years of hand-crafted black oak. The cracked linoleum floor shines under heavy new coats of shellac gassing off thick sharp fumes. Eye-level windows opposite the bookshelf filter a grey light. My memory is telling me her sweater is yellow.

  'Ma'am, who is that?' I ask.

'Where?'

'The woman looking at books.'

'Oh, I don't know. How long has she been there?'

'All morning.'

'Actually, I think she's one of the people who choose to walk the halls in front of the bookcases.'

'Who is standing behind her?'

A woman fitted in cruel, ill-fitting wool looks over her shoulder. She leans down and carefully removes a book from a lower shelf.

  'Who is that?' I ask again.

'There is a woman standing there, isn't there? I've never noticed her before.'

  'I've seen her with other people doing this.'

'You know you can hold any of the books here.'

'I know.'

'Just return them undamaged.'

'So the woman just gets to hold the book?'

'I believe she's being asked to remember if she has read that book on the lower shelf.'

The woman in wool places the book back in the glass cabinet.

'Oh, see there, she can't remember if she's read that book.'

'She can't read it again?'

'If you remember reading it, you get to hold it.'

'But you can't read it again.'

'No. She remembers how to read.'

'But not what she's read.'

'Precisely.'

The caretaker assigned to me is merry and means well. Not bouncy, but always speaks with a smile. The building is beautiful. Old but bright, tall beautiful windows everywhere. Marble and wood and gorgeous art well cared for, picture carpets on the walls. I have my own desk that's been a desk to other people for two hundred years. I'm lucky I guess. Coming here was a good decision. Not sure of the state of things I left behind, but this all feels right.

'OK, now we need to help you to not go a little funny in the head while you nativise.'

She lays out beautiful blank papers and fine pens.

'I requested pencils.'

'Of course, I have them right here for you.'

Beautiful, beautiful pencils.

'Later, we'll let you know which sentences must be written in pen. Pencils are just for fun.'

'OK. So, I start with a kind of confession? Is that what I heard?'

'No. You're not signing a contract.'

'And I can leave.'

'You can leave this room, into the hallway. You can go wherever you like, whenever you like.'

'Right. Just stay inside.'

'Yea, well, you can go outside. But, look it's right here. The outside is beautiful.'

'It really is.'

'It's never been this beautiful. That's why we have all these windows.'

'So all this is working?'

'It works so well.'

Her smile seems genuine, though there is a saliva crust in one corner of her mouth. She's been talking a lot. I'm pretty sure she's assigned to many other people.

'I do want you to know that you can leave at any time.'

'But there's nothing out there.'

'What do you mean?'

'Food, shelter, entertainment.'

'Not really.'

'Everyone's in here now.'

'Most are in here now, yes.'

'Could I get back in if I leave?'

'Yes, of course. You wouldn't come back to me, however.'

'Somebody else is in charge of that?'

'Not, in charge, exactly.'

'Just helpful.'

'Yes.'

Is she giving me the wrong information?

'This is what you want, correct?' she asks.

'It's really working?'

'Look outside.'

'Beautiful.'

'It's never been this beautiful.'

'I really do have to relieve myself, now.'

'Right. Just click that latch under your chair and that will drop open the lavatory trap. Is the back fly in your trousers open?'

'Yes.'

'OK, just push your merry gentleman down between your legs and aim well. I'll turn around.'

I piss into the shallow toilet in the floor under my chair.

'Better?'

'Not really.'

I'm a young man but was never prepared for much of anything. I can read and write. I can fix minor issues with sinks and toilets. Change a light fixture and swap out the flat tyres on my bicycle. Trim trees. I like animals and talking to friends on phones. But with the death of my parents, the loss of a dream job and the creep of black mould I discovered in a basement closet of my new home, I had no idea what to do next. I gave it all up and came to the *Great and Spacious Building Retirement Company*. I am twenty-nine years old.

The accommodations are nice enough. People are very pleasant. Food is prepared properly and quite delicious. The lodging fee is reasonable and costs much less than being alone in a house with a cat that doesn't give two shits about me. I left the door open for her. I hope she finds a new home. I've been asked to sit at my desk with pens and pencils and this very nice paper. As yet, there is no required writing. I am to take my meals here as well. One new person a day comes and sits with me while I eat. They say nothing. New bed sheets and towels weekly. No one answers any of my questions yet. This silence, they tell me, is to create loneliness so that in a few weeks when I join groups of people in the various planned activities, I'll be pleasant and genuinely interested in the lives of others. I look forward to that very much.

The first weeks have ended. I can now go onto the deck extending out from my room. I'm lucky to be on the ground floor. A young man meets me here with a cup of coffee. Deck boys too?! Cloudless, brilliantly blue sky. Snow still deep in the tall white mountains rising above the conifers in the distance. Mostly men here in this section, except for the woman next door to me who's just arrived. Not sure where the rest of them are or what they're up to. Not too concerned about that. Less trouble and anxiety. At least for now.

There's more beauty here than I would have expected. I'm less frightened about growing old in this room. The young man pours me a glass of water from a carafe on the small deck table.

'Can you see into the distance there,' I ask. 'My eyes are a bit fuzzy.'

The young man nods.

'Are there things happening up there still.'

He smiles and nods and leaves with the empty bottle.

'Excuse me, can you just wait here for a moment. I'd like to walk away and I want you to yell after me as soon as I'm out of sight. The second you can't see me wave both your arms.'

He smiles.

'Then I'll know how far away I can go.'

Of course, it wasn't very far. Across a small meadow to a border of dark trees. The cedar forest is as all the stories describe. The damp smell of sweet leather. The faint delicate songs of what, of course, must be small invisible birds. Fern forested floor. Small blue flowers. Fingers of cool, wet sunlight. But no food or music or women or pens or paper.

I step into the dark line of trees and quickly turned. The deck boy sets down my new bedding and frantically waves both arms above his head. I have exactly three minutes to decide. To stay under the canopy of welcoming red cedar, without any knowledge of how to stay alive or to quickly step back within sight of the young man and know that at least there will be food and shelter for the rest of my life. Die here in solitude or learn to live with loneliness.

I look up to take in the whole of the Great and Spacious Building. People standing in so many windows.

*

So, Kafka? That's what I'm reading here, correct? A nicer, more humane Kafka. A Kafka with a conscience. Kafka with windows. There really aren't any more stories to tell are there? You could write about helping me dress my wounds. Or letting the dogs in and out of the kitchen door a hundred times a day. Or making my soft food. Or being someone who never found love. You want some sting in what you write because you're missing that sting in your one-walk-a-day life. The sting or that scratching sound you think is always there that you think others want to read about. You have some clever conceit waiting don't you? I can see it coming a mile away. That part you have figured out and I know what it is within the first four lines. Why write this if you know where it's going? Be a fiction writer not a goddamn pamphleteer.

This is M's third written review of the introductory paragraph of my possible new novel. Third draft maybe. He speaks less and less now. Not because he can't. But because he's lost most his hearing and says he doesn't want to sound like a retard when he talks.

He scribbled this critique on the inside of the back cover he tore off the copy of *Fahrenheit 451* I got him from a thrift shop. I guess he has a point. I already know how I want this story to end.

M is the first letter of his name. By law I can't reveal anything else about him. I'm paid to keep his healthcare a secret. Disturbing, maybe even criminal things are starting to happen. His rapid hearing loss was unexpected. No one knows what is causing it. He ventures into the pasture across the street more now than ever.

This morning he's in the middle of the road scraping the flattened racoon carcass off the road with the flat square shovel I use to edge the grass away from the sidewalk. He brings it back to the porch.

'No babies with her?' I ask.

'I didn't see any. Will the dogs eat this?'

'Don't feed that to the dogs, please.'

He dumps the body into the plastic bin and falls into his patio chair next to me. The bandage on his leg bleeds.

'You popped your stitches again.'

'What?'

I say it again, louder.

He looks at his leg and isn't surprised. How could he be? He understands body fluids more than any client I've had. When he comes back from the wooded glen at the back of the pasture there is often blood under his fingernails. When I change his bandages and flush the infection from his wounds, he stays alarmingly still. Even falls asleep on occasion. Mostly just stares across the street into the pasture and counts the geese as they come and go.

'Do you have anything else for me to read?'

I know we've entered the end chapter of his hospice. I fear these final days will be the worst I've had.

'I'll get you something after I clear out this cupboard.'

Two whole shelves in one cupboard are filled with the collection of coffee and hot chocolate mugs left behind by my last client. I never fully understood the difference. Each is stamped with a cute graphic and a cheeky phrase. These were her Christmas gifts every year or her only purchases at the flea market. She was the last person anyone ever thought of. The quality of the presents she gave and received matched the status of the people around her. Mass produced and mundane.

Each mug has a pithy, snide comment printed over pictures of mid-century housewives or cartoon characters. I suppose those are the same things. She was a trauma nurse for twenty years, in and out of rehab. Lost her licence. Gave the wrong medication to people. Drove drunk in cars without licence plates. Several hit and run accidents. At the very back of the cupboard hidden behind the black Mickey Mouse cup, I discover the mug carrying a picture of her dead father. White cowboy hat, purple striped shirt with pearl buttons tucked into a shiny rodeo belt buckle. A gaunt opioid addict who facilitated her molestations and demanded she be the one to take care of him as he convalesced. When he slipped into a coma, she was the one who decided to pull the plug.

Do I throw them away, smash them on the sidewalk? These cheap and easy pieces of a person's life. I never know what to do with the odds and ends my clients leave behind. I'm not very good with endings. I leave the mugs on the counter and hand over another paragraph to M.

*

After three weeks of sitting in silence across from new strangers every day who deliver my meals, I was ready for group gatherings. Sufficiently lonely and longing for human speech I was appointed to participate in the Rectification of Undeserved Criticisms reading group. This was a literary group discussing all negative critiques of great works of art that were unduly harsh and damaging to literature that were later deemed to have remarkable social value and skill. But the night before, I wrote down the following dream.

I dreamed of a goddess eating her children. I walked across the small meadow outside my room and stopped at the edge of the forest. She was there, sat up against a towering sequoia, bare breasted, dripping grease and gristle onto her bloated stomach.

'Why should it be the case that my eyes bulge at the taste of human flesh?' she asked. 'You'll forgive my hairy ancestors. Those flattened animals in the middle of your byways are nothing so much as what it means to survive. I am no greater than those. In the end, I'll be just as silent and spun round.'

These were not Jonathan Swift babies, pale and thinned by poverty. These babies were shiny and plump. Pink, smiling and well-fed. Happily kicking their chubby legs, presented to her on beds of lettuce. Grilled fatty limbs and buttocks. Not dragged to the spits forcefully or taken in haste but left curbside by their wealthy parents, exhausted by their demanding appetites.

Here's what the reader will think during this section: You murderous prick! How dare you use children as a grotesque literary device. Writing doesn't untether people from their frail sympathies, my friend. For most suckers, human flesh means something much more than what simply burns and blemishes. You're asking them to confront an impossible question. Are we more than worms? You're never going to convince people that the sacred doesn't exist. Lazy!

M is collecting the clippings of horse hooves left in the pasture across the street by the horse farrier. He boils them on the stove in a giant cast iron pot he found curbside to make gelatin. He cooked a goose he said he found already dead in the same pot. I've never seen an already-dead Canadian goose. They're smart as hell. They don't die accidentally. And no, they don't taste good. No one has a recipe to make wild waterfowl delicious. Fuck off with your Dr. Pepper marinade!

I'm sure he strangled it, swung it over his head to snap its neck, boiled it and scraped off the feathers with a butter knife and is now convinced the pasture is an unending supply of natural protein. Convinced he had discovered the secret to make wild food palatable, he set a fancy table for the two of us. The surprised look of suppressed horror on the face of an arrogant, dying human male as he chews the first gamey bite – that's the true heart of every story ever told.

'The winters here are so mild now these fuckers think this is as far south as they need to go,' is what I think he said with a mouth full of chewy goose flesh.

He never admits that the meat tastes like mud. He tries convincing me he's given up the stomach for spiced food and that he survives by consuming edibles from the pasture. He makes sure I see him chewing on rose hips and the wild asparagus on mornings when I come out onto the porch for morning coffee. There's a neighbour's neglected apple tree in one corner and a cherry tree in the other. But he's goddamned obese. There aren't enough cherries in this city to keep him alive. But maybe silence and fasting are serving him a similar purpose. But he's not fooling me. I hear him rummaging through the neighbour's garbage bins at night. After nearly thirty years of caring for the nearly dead, I'm tired of micromanaging. I let him be.

I see him wandering the pasture in that purple darkness of twilight. To watch witches hover over the milkweed and pinch open monarch butterfly cocoons. He sits in the dry dirt of the horses' dust bath, hunched and straight-legged and stares at the silhouette of the dead honey locust. In cryptic notes left where I can find them, he claims things are being revealed to him.

There is something showing itself to me the longer I don't speak. Of course, I can't tell you what it is. Just know, it's no big deal.

He was told twenty years ago to get hearing aids. Couldn't be bothered. The accident shook loose what delicate gears were left in his ears and now there's no sound but the bellows of his own gut.

There's a soft clicking in my bones, feels like tiny bubbles rising up the fluid in my spinal column. Sounds like scuba.

The coffee mugs left by the alcoholic nurse are lined up on the counter this morning as I come out for coffee. M has placed three small notes in front of them. It looks like a eulogy. Or a treasure map. I can't tell which. The black Mickey Mouse mug is first. Then,

From scratch? Why yes, I scratched the label right off the baking box.

I don't remember asking for your opinion.

Whatever, I'm still fabulous.

Shh, there's wine in here.

Martinis aren't just for breakfast anymore.

I dare not drink from any of them. The mug with the picture of her father on it is missing. Seems a shame to split them up. I could request that Good Will sell them as a set. But then this story would make little sense unless the buyer knew how she died. We all want our endings explained.

They call my home a halfway house. Halfway to what? I've always wondered. Most of my clients died here in this two-bedroom apartment. They were way past halfway. The weights of the world. The overburdens. The gout in their ankles. The extra sugar in their veins. The swollen murmurs in their chests. The flattened streams of blood up the backs of their legs. Their soft bones and confused ideas. All concretions of some steady, sticky drip that humans can't turn off.

I step onto the porch with my coffee. M's drinking from the Cup of the Opioid Cowboy. He's keeping the origin of a stranger's story for himself. I hand him back his notes one by one. I'm convinced these are the last three things he will ever write.

A honey bee in a glass jar.

I asked him what that means. He points to his heart.

The grind of rock salt in a pepper mill.

He points back to his heart, then to his ear. What his heart sounds like now that he's lost his hearing.

Swallow the small to heal the immortal.

He smiles and takes this note, tears it up and pushes the pieces into his shirt pocket.

We've both gone silent now. No more reviews of my fiction or snarky notes or even single words on scraps of paper. Instead he hums. I assume to cover up the uneven sounds of his dying heart. In the morning the hums are short and breathy as he dresses. He constantly pulls at the collars of all his shirts. Too tight, and he can feel the pulse of blood in the veins of his neck.

His hums are steady and soft when he watches the flat curls of cold cream on the surface of his hot coffee. His hums are a waltz when he traces the tip of his finger along the scratches in the old oak tabletop left from the many bewildered fingernails belonging to people who knew they had come to my home to pass away.

When the pasture floods from spring runoff he crosses the street and crawls under the barbed wire to sit on the soggy ground to watch dragonflies. He pauses the humming, but spends the hour placing two fingers at different places of his chest as he deeply breathes. Then at his wrists to count the pulses of blood.

A lot of throat clearing at lunch. Then a low, deep rumbling hum in the evening as he lays in bed. When he sleeps, the fits come in troubled frequencies. Uh, uh! Uh, uh! Shuffling to lay quiet and comfortable, trying desperately to escape the soft shudders from the growing number of skipped and irregular heartbeats. Some nights he wakes pounding his chest. They said his heart will eventually stop. I have the number to call when it does.

This is now an apartment full of real witches and floating shadows. The fly caught in the screen door. The dust rising and falling in the morning slivers of sunlight across this dark old table. The rotting lemon. The stains of wine and tobacco on a kitchen towel printed with dogs in Halloween costumes. M is my last ward. My own infirmities have taken hold. The stories I write now are meant only for me.

*

In a better world she belongs to Rubens. Though not nude, she is transparent and rosy and shines with sweet perspiration. Each week she pulls her fresh linens off her bed and piles them on her deck next door. Her hair is a bouquet of light caramel curls, her laughter is raucous and she hums sweet familiar tunes that have long forgotten titles. She is often at the edge of the meadow gathering sticks and fern fronds to weave into her crown of curls. She is silly and talks to herself in different accents. She is what people used to call mad. But at the Great and Spacious Building she is left to wander where she likes with as many bottles of wine as she requests. She visits each deck at ground level and offers each occupant a quick pull off her bottles. Some accept, many do not.

When she's had her fill, she dances away from the building across the meadow and relieves herself at the edge of the trees. Her deck boy has fashioned several long colourful streamers to the end of a long pole to wave as the warning to return from the cedar glens when she steps out of sight.

She learns to scale the wall on the outside of the building. I have noticed recently the many small ledges and handholds curiously built into the masonry. She easily moves up and down, side to side, visiting each of the porches connected to the many thousand rooms. I have never been able to accurately count the floors to this building. Most days she climbs so high that I lose sight of her. She carries the bottles of wine and leafy sticks and fruit I have never seen or can identify, in a large canvas bag strapped to her back. She invites the people who come out to greet her to eat and drink with her. Some do. Many don't. Some sing with her. Fewer dance. Some grab at her and try to pull her into their rooms. Men mostly. She always refuses. Some want to hold her as they cry. She listens briefly to their stories, then pats them on the head and moves on. But none so far have left their porches to climb with her.

When she looks at me as she returns from her daily sojourns, she sees me with wooden eyes. She knows I wear an uncomfortable skin. My stone-cloistered constitution is why, I believe, she has not offered me wine or sticks for my hair. She is too much a clown for my liking, too happy and joyous without cause. I prefer a more even silliness. When I come out to watch the sun set and she is there on her porch, she will turn to me and bow deeply, but never approach. Though I don't want her to come over to me, I still feel sad that she has not tried.

I request the same food and wine she has. It all comes straight away. I was never told that I could do this. I raise a quiet glass to her when she looks exhausted and I'm certain she'll not join me.

Others are out and climb the building now. They hang from dangled ropes and weave hammocks that swing from porch to porch. Three people have fallen to their deaths. Many come to her deck with gifts and well wishes to thank and praise her, but she doesn't receive them. She doesn't make any angry announcements, but everyone soon understands she is not to be disturbed. The outside of the Great and Spacious Building is now covered with rope ladders and suspended baskets of flowering plants and vegetables and musicians and beds for small animals. I still do not want another cat.

She sees me writing most every day. She looks at me without the broad smile now. When I raise my glass, she nods simply. She acquired a telescope, binoculars and a medical kit. I requested the same and received the same. I was never told I could do that. She's packed a bag and stands by it. She is dressed in thick and colourful clothing. Her head is lowered, her eyes are wide and her mouth nurses a tiny smirk. She speaks to herself. Her sentences are quiet murmurs like cricket legs or moth wings around a flickering porch light. Her soft speech trails behind her in easy, gentle waves as she walks away into the cedar trees. I want to believe that I can see her words rise up and stretch across the stone face of the Great and Spacious Building where they will etch themselves into this monolith. I know that's impossible. I want to believe the sounds of her purl crowd the cracks and the crevices and peel back the paint on the planks of each porch. I know they don't. Her words are plain and pot-bellied and none of them can be written down. I count the seconds and wonder if she'll return in time.

This story is also available as an audio version read by the author.
See page 241 for more details, or visit dark-mountain.net/issue-18-fabula-audio

Illustration by **Bethan McFadden**

Constant Comment

Kim Goldberg

The hobo in my teacup shakes his fist and shouts at me every morning as I pour the boiling water in. He takes cover behind the teabag then makes it his life raft as the rising sea lofts him to the top, blathering all the way. Last week I thought I heard him yell 'climate change.' Other times, names of dead presidents, Shakespeare's missing sonnets, a recipe for baked halibut. My therapist says these are projections of my Inner Dialogue with my Angry Fractal Self. Yet the halibut was divine. I embark on a journey to the Golden Fridge over a tricky path of loose hypotheses above the treeline. Even my burro protests. When I return with the milk, the hobo is gone like a mob of pigeons. Ceasing to exist when each bird bursts off in a new direction.

This story is also available as an audio version read by the author.
See page 241 for more details, or visit dark-mountain.net/issue-18-fabula-audio

Meeting Jeff Bezos

Siana Fitzjohn

The door closed behind me with a click.

'Mr. Bezos! Thank you so much for meeting me, I can't tell you how grateful I am...'

Mr. Bezos smiled and shook my hand.

'Please, call me Jeff. Come, come, take a seat.'

I looked around the vast, stylish lounge, with large windows and an open-plan kitchen at one end, bright yellow lights hanging from the high ceiling.

'This place is—'

'Thank you, thank you, yes we love it here!'

Said Jeff, sitting himself opposite me on a black leather sofa.

'Now, you're here to write an article about me for that magazine, yes?'

'Well it's about the challenges young entrepreneurs face in this new—'

'What young entrepreneurs need is some good advice.'

Said Jeff stretching one hand along the back of the seat.

'Lesson one, be inspired, think outside the circle. Always. Look at things freshly, with a beginner's mind!'

I began to take notes.

'Thank you Mr. Be – Jeff, but I wanted to ask you about—'

'Lesson two! Be proud, not of your gifts but of your hard work and your choices. For example, I was gifted an amazing butt.'

'Excuse me?'

Jeff continued.

'My butt, it's beautiful. But I can't be proud of my butt, it's a gift.

But to use my gift in the most inspirational and futuristic way possible, THAT requires hard work, and wise choices.'

Jeff looked at me keenly.

'Sorry Jeff, I'm not sure I understand what you—'

He slapped his knees and leaned forward.

'One of my jobs, as leader of Amazon, is to encourage people to be bold.'

Jeff stood up suddenly, and walked into the kitchen. He slid a long knife out of its block, pulled down his pants and cut a thick slice of flesh from his right buttock.

I screamed. Jeff was already talking.

'Lesson three. You have to be leaning into the future. If you're leaning away from the future the future is going to win every time.'

He walked calmly towards my chair.

'Pig's bacon is on its way out – the vegans saw to that. So, what do inventors like me do? We think of something NEW.'

He looked into my eyes, and held the round slice of buttock up to my face.

'Never, ever, ever lean away from the future.'

He said earnestly.

'Jesus Christ,'

I panted in shock.

'There's blood dripping all over your—'

'Carpet?'

Jeff winked.

'No, no, you won't find carpets in here. Lesson four. Work on marble floors as much as possible. Carpets lead to drama. Spills create fluster. I don't need fluster in my life. Take it from me – marble floors. Minimise the mess.'

'But Jeff you're bleeding quite a lot...'

'Lesson five. You need to be nimble and robust – you need to be able to take a punch. Look at my ass, it's nimble, trim, but it's also —'

'Robust...'

I said weakly. Jeff smiled.

'Exactly.'

He was walking back towards the kitchen. Taking a pan from the cupboard, he turned on the stove and heated some oil. He lay the sliver of buttock into the pan with a sizzle.

'Lesson six. Don't over complicate a good thing. Once you have something good – really good – you don't want to spoil it by adding too much. See, to my butt I'm just going to add a crunch of salt—'

He gave the salt grinder an exaggerated twist.

'And a drizzle of...honey.'

He poured honey with flourish.

'There! Smell that glazing up nicely?'

I took a sniff.

'I do.'

Jeff took a plate from a glass cabinet.

'Lesson seven. Learn to take hits from you opponents. Turn your failures around. I've had my ass handed to me loads of times – now look at me! I'm handing it to myself!'

He grinned widely, flipping the crispy glazed rasher onto the plate.

'Mr. Bezos, I really must—'

'Please, it's Jeff. Now, remember. It's easy to have ideas.'

He turned off the stove and came to place the plate on the coffee table between us.

'I mean look at me, frying up my own ass – nobody does that! It's completely inspired. But it's very hard to turn great ideas into a successful product.'

He began sharpening a knife. Then, tenderly, he cut the buttock into strips.

'If I were to market my ass, I would need a marketing campaign, media strategy, production plan, good lawyers, insurance ... it's not plain sailing. It's *hard* work. Now, try a piece.'

'Mr. Bezos, I really don't think I—'

'Oh, come now! Live a little.'

Said Jeff, popping a slice of his ass into his mouth and closing his eyes.

'Delicious! Can't believe I haven't tried this before. Are you sure you don't care for some?'

'I really can't—'

'Really? Suit yourself.'

Jeff put another piece into his mouth.

'So sweet, yet salty … and juicy yet, crisp. A gift, I tell you.'

He sighed, chewing appreciatively.

'Now,'

He swallowed.

'The real key to being an entrepreneur is knowing how and where to push yourself. What's the one marketing platform where people would buy anything – even Jeff Bezos' ass?'

I gulped.

'Amazon?'

Jeff took the last piece of ass with his fork, touching it gently to his lips before putting it slowly, deliberately into his mouth. His eyes glinted.

'You got it.'

'Mr. Bezos, thank you so much for your time, I really must be going.'

I rose and strode quickly to the door.

'Wait! One more thing…Entrepreneurs need to Work. Their. Ass. Off. There are many steps to being successful, and you want to take those steps with passion and ferocity. Look at me, look at me!'

I looked. Jeff Bezos was grinning.

'I'm passionate, but I'm also ferocious.'

His grin grew wider and wild-eyed.

'Passionate. But also, I'm ferocious.'

This story is also available as an audio version read by the author.
See page 241 for more details, or visit dark-mountain.net/issue-18-fabula-audio

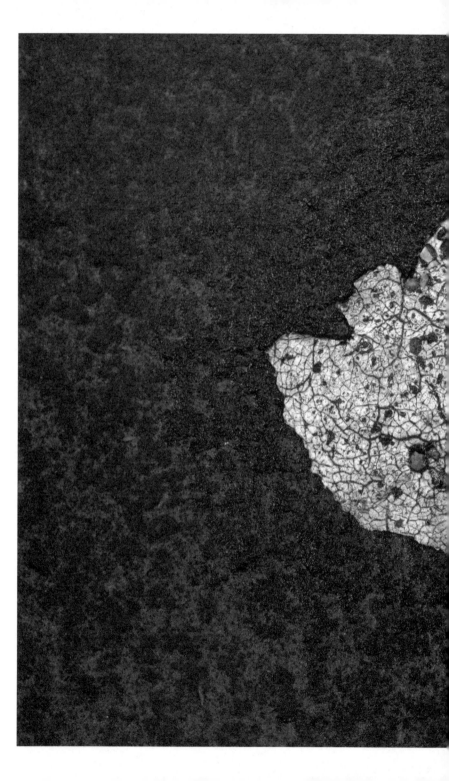

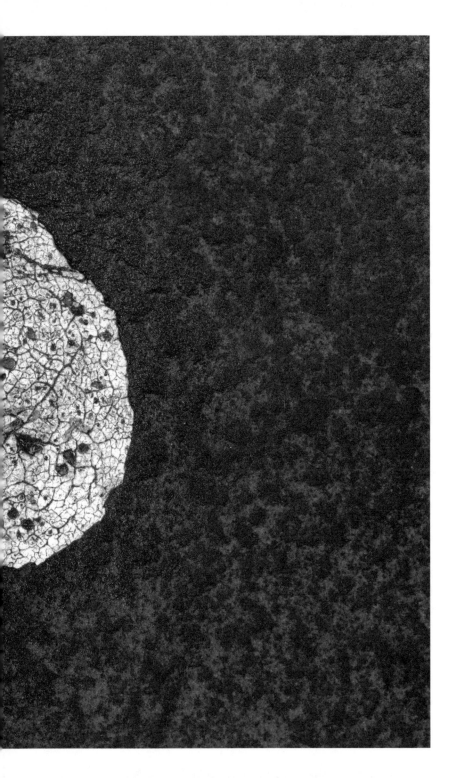

Effie Paleologou

From the *Microcosms* series: Aerial view #9,

Black and White Photograph on Hahnemühle Photo Rag, 2013–17

Flux

Luke Winter

Blustering through the world of dark, massed wings scissored the silence apart. The moon's light spilled from behind a cloud, illuminating the chopping of a hundred-thousand butterflies as they blew high over the sea.

In the Four Arms in Northumberland, Generous Pete, two feet deep in a miracle of compassion, is buying a round for Michael the flat-earther.

Steve, behind the bar, so far would have heard Flat Michael elucidate his peculiar take on his ideas enough times to count sheep to sleep, had he been counting. But Steve had not been counting. He gave a half smile as he passed Flat Michael on Pete's pity pint.

The bubbles in the lager fizzed, their hands wrapped round the pints, the night wrapped round the pub, and the butterflies approached.

Some said it had been the storm gusts disrupting the migration patterns. Others rehashed old superstitions. Michael stuck to the facts, they had been clear enough. Steve turned up the television that hung over the corner of the bar. 'Said local landlord J. Superhans.'

'That's time gentlemen.' Steve shouted, and pressed a button next to the glass washer marked 'close'. A taxidermied squirrel span on a small podium between the spirits bottles. LED lights giddied around the podium's base.

Flat Michael wanted a bell for last orders, which only made Steve more fond of the corpse. The face of the squirrel appeared from behind its broad, erect tail as the podium rotated.

'An absinthe and a bucks fizz.'

'Fuck off. Bar's closed Michael.'

'You've barely called it. H'way man.' Michael's weather reddened face pointed up at him.

Up from his stool, Pete ferreted baccy into a skin. He unhooked his coat from below the bar and hoisted it back round himself. He laboured with the buttons until each slotted home, lipped his ponytail into his hood, and his hood over his head. The coat sagged down until Pete was only a bristly chin, eight fingers and one rolled up fag. He raised his hand to Steve and Flat Michael in benediction, turned and pulled at the door to the Four Arms. It opened like a greyhound's cage, and through it gusted shapes of clustered, blustering black.

The door ajar, tenebrous shapes billowing from its open edge, Pete turned. He had his shoulder to the door, then his back to it. With a great punt he got it shut again.

Dancing, fizzling shadows now filled the pub. Glitches of light would appear; an eye of Michael, the top of a beer tap, a button off a jukebox.

'Flutterflies' mumbled Michael. He swiped his hands through the air in front of him, walking blindly towards where he knew the hatch to the bar lay. There was a brief cry, a fall, then Michael was fumbling backwards, smearing the air with his hands. 'You think I was born yesterday Flat Michael?' Shouted Steve from the floor in front of the drinks fridges.

With nothing else to do, Pete lit his fag. A shield of blue smoke began to press outward around him. Pete sucked harder. The orange cherry glowed. The baccy cracked and spat, and blue smoke plumed from Pete's lips. The smoke grew around him, and no butterfly broached it.

'Fags lads, roll yourselves fags,' shouted Pete.

Flat Michael stumbled towards the sound of Pete's voice, taking himself out over a chair. Sucking the fag between his lips, Pete used two hands to flurry tobacco into papers. Michael's yelps grew nearer. The din of wings of butterflies did not eclipse the sound of a clipper lighter being flicked, and Steve cursing purple somewhere amongst it.

Pete licked a second roll-up shut and began puffing. Michael huffed into Pete's shield, continuing to paw at the air in front of him, swapping butterflies for dense smoke. Pete passed Flat Michael the fag and began rolling a third.

Steve pushed against the seething wings, hands in front of his eyes and mouth. As he broached the blue bubble of smoke, he was passed a lit cigarette by Pete, who now dangled a fag from either end of his mouth like a carcinogenic vampire.

The surfaces of the Four Arms had dissolved. Everything was woozy with movement. Wings beat smoke and smoke tangled wings. The three men stood.

'What's this? I reckon we turn the heating off, seal the windows, leave them to it,' coughed Michael.

'You've to ring the council. They send pest control' said Pete.

A butterfly chopped into the smoke towards him. Pete held out a finger. It landed and clung to it, as if it had found a branch amid a flood. The butterfly was little bigger than a fifty pence piece.

'Don't think the council's much use at this hour,' said Steve.

'How long will they be outside?'

'Dawn,' said Pete, and blew a jet of blue smoke at the butterfly on his finger. It flopped off, and lolloped on sloppy wings away from the smoke.

'We're as well pulling the curtains over us and kipping here. Outside'll be mental. You won't be able to get up main street. Your farm's a million miles away in this Michael. I heard about it happening in Wiltshire and Stroud. Not here like.'

'Has one of yous got a GPS Mag on yez?' asked Steve.

'I've not bothered with them.'

'Aye I'm not daft.'

'They reckon it's them sending nature doolally,' said Steve.

'Whey of course it is. My pigeons when I raced them, you get to know them like yeh kids. You cannit just say all homing pigeons are the same. If you take one part of their DNA and plug it into some other creature, that's not going to work,' said Pete.

'Aye, but they think of nature as a machine. They reckon we're built from modules, and they can swap modules arounds like parts in motor,' said Michael.

'Whey is that working how they'd hoped?' Pete passed round more rollups.

'It's not them that's caused this they're saying. They're saying its bats again. But organic drones appear, and then these mad swarms start happening.'

'They're saying the birds have had their migration routes thrown off.'

'Not just birds, where's these butterflies from? I've never seen one like these here,' said Flat Michael.

'Aye man but they said that with 5G that it was sending the cats nuts. But that calmed down,' said Pete.

'It's them Organic Delivery Drones. I'm not one for conspiracy theories but,' Steve sucked at his fag.

'GPS Mags fucking with migration patterns?'

'Something is.' Michael was squinting, either from disgust or asphyxiation.

'They learn off each other. What one member of a species learns, the easier it becomes for the rest of them to pick up. Morphic resonance. They've done scientific studies. Rupert Sheldrake. Look it up,' said Michael.

'Well I wouldn't be surprised if these butterflies are the late tail following someone's drone delivery.'

'Are they stupid?'

'Drones were just robots eh? Before these mutant pigeons.'

'Seagulls.'

'Aye, whey, DNA from both. Strength of a seagull, direction of a homing pigeon,' said Pete.

'And no eyes,' chimed Michael.

'Have you heard about eagles eating them? I seen a video. People are scared the eagles might start genetic mutations and that now.' Steve ignored Michael's horror.

'They didn't change the name. You notice that? Drones they still call them.'

'Whey Huel fed eyeless mutants doesn't roll off the tongue,' said Pete.

'Aye it was the GPS Mags they marketed. How cheap and easy it was. Take your Mag out the case, press the button, and drones will drop off your order. Fossil fuel free. No mention of mutants.'

'Mental.'

'Someone in the village will have gotten one.'

'H'way Steve. Crack out the Sambuca,' said Michael.

Around the Four Arms, under the light of the moon, the blizzard of butterflies thickened. The deluge shimmered along decreasing stars.

In a research depot, at the roosts, a homing pigeon pondered with its head on a slant. A drone screeched. Despite its well-winged travels, this homing pigeon could not understand its neighbour's tongue. The pigeon had heard the Glasgow patter of the Clydeside racers. It knew the Geordie gabble of the Tyne. It had heard the Scouse smur, the Cork craic, the Basque brogue, the Morroccan fizzle. But the drones spoke like no other bird. The drone screeched again, flurried its wings into roosting flaps, shat, and settled down. A mechanical tube whined, and the shit was sucked away.

From the bowels of the depot, from racks of rows, similar screeches rebounded as other drones settled in to be shut down. The lights in block 12C went out.

In fulfillment unit 12D, twenty-two thousand drones were about to be woken with LED light and a feed injection. Outside the sound-proofed hanger, you would hear a high-pitched boil as the program booted them up. At any one time, one hundred thousand drones were operational. By year two of the phased deployment, a million active units were planned. If the researchers could find a way to mitigate the lice.

Fossil Free Delivery
Faster. More Accurate. Planet Friendly.
Zero Carbon. Maximum speed.
Nozama Corp

In a country lane of hawthorn hedges adjacent to the town of Wirral, Robin Stew nicked a bolt into his crossbow. He stared up to the drone's feathered belly, and squinted. Even if it knew he was there, and Robin had been careful to ensure that no one knew anything of this escapade, the drone would not blink. No fight or flight reactions had been selected for their DNA. No sex organs. They'd edited the eyes out from their mutants too. The sockets remained in the skeletal system, but the face had a smooth slope of feathers, interrupted only by the beak.

The specimen upon which Robin's crossbow was trained was one of the newer units. Its plumage hue had been dialled down from the twitter-cyan of the betas, to this naval-grey. Hawks had taken too many of the first birds. £85k each they cost Nozama Corp. Three times what Robin had been paid per year as a delivery driver. The crossbow cost £200. Robin's kill count was seventy-six. It was about to go up one. His was the second highest count within the Merseyside Avenger cell. With the gentlest squeeze he hugged the trigger towards his chest.

Above the Four Arms in Northumberland, a drone mobbed by butterflies made little progress. The butterflies pushed towards the point it inhabited, suffocating its space. A mass of wings squashed together, pushing against the bodies above them. The whole tangled mass, a flapping mess, falling towards the earth.

'Activists protesting Nozama Corp's use of genetically modified delivery drones have stormed a depot in Staffordshire. Protestors claim that Nozama Corp's creation and treatment of the creatures is unethical. They allege working conditions for the creatures to equate to animal cruelty. Nozama Corp denies the allegations and maintains that its drones are not sentient. Four people have been arrested.'

The drone's ribcage shone like teeth. The cavity that had once been its chest was lined with butterflies. Cocoons dangled from its inter-costal muscles. Laying beneath the carcass, amongst the grass, the surface of a GPS Mag reflected the leaden dawn, smooth but for the etching of Nozama Corp's logo.

As morning broached the Four Arms, Pete's snaffled snores returned Michael from his dreams. Rectangles of amber light hung across the wall. Paintings of hunting parties, caked in dust were fringed by roosting butterflies.

Michael turned onto his side. The curtain that covered him rustled and cracked. His left arm speared from under the covers and clutched an uncorked bottle of Sambuca. He tilted the bottle to his mouth. Liquid burst from the bottle's neck, swamping his lips, and ran thick and sticky over his chin.

This story is also available as an audio version read by the author.
See page 241 for more details, or visit dark-mountain.net/issue-18-fabula-audio

Oxen

Cynan Jones

Illustrations by **Nick Hayes**

A searing wind snapped at their coat collars and hoods, a sound not natural on the moor, clipped and sharp as it was, within such expanse.

'What is it?' Iohan asked.

The two men stood at the edge of the pit.

The heavy skulls of cows; the horns – where skulls still had them – seemed made of wood charred black.

Only some of the ribcages remained in shape, strange carnivorous gin traps amongst the fallen bone.

The pelvises, discoloured, looked formed from flint. The spines discarded from some mechanic function.

'I don't know,' answered Mal, the larger brother. 'I don't know what it is.' His eyes watered in the wind, so it seemed he cried to see this charnel.

The wind was of such force the patches of scrub willow and birch looked gripped by an invisible great beast, intent to rip the re-established trees out by their roots.

The brothers, in their heavy coats, appeared weighted to the hill. Leant into the wind.

And yet the boneyard seemed impervious.

'Dad will know.'

————

The felled turbine had landed on the uneven ground with a hollow pang then bounced, as if it meant to bolt away over the crest, and in doing so flicked away the cap of earth that had grown over the pit.

The cap lay peeled back from the ground now, like some scab that had been lifted off intact.

The cone-point of the nacelle had smashed into a discard of fist-sized stones that seemed – amongst the moss, the wiry grass and the scratching whin and heather – to have no place there. They looked spilled from some tipped-up wheelbarrow. Trundled by giants over the moor.

Each stone was felted with lichen, green, grey-frayed and ochre-patched like the different topographies of an atlas. It made Iohan imagine maps. That the stones showed ways to other worlds.

When they started the cermet-tip saws, to cut the steel mast into sections, the horrifying sound of them drove all thought away.

The spits of bright hot metal died to wet leaves against their coats.

Puffs of dust-smoke went off in the wind, the ochre of the lichen.

The rust smudged like red clay.

The moorland, darkened through the brothers' visors, seemed some-how to flex. That muscle moved beneath its skin. As if they worked upon the back of some huge animal.

With the ear defenders, Iohan believed he heard his own brain. Could change the squeal of the saw if he changed the shape of his mouth, gaped, like a strange fish, popped his lips.

Where the ground had eroded, the giant turbine bases came through the moor like the broken stumps of back teeth.

The huge molars of the skulls.

They had talked about trying to wrench the metal reinforcements from the concrete but knew they would not. That the bases would stay, the energy companies dissipated into air before they had to rectify their mess.

Had talked of dynamite. The presence of the box that of a treasure chest.

Each stick bagged, seepage salted on the clouded plastic; the cardboard wrappings perished; the license of procurement, for quarrying on the farm, twice renewed, five years each time, long ago expired.

Iohan thought now of the dynamite, of the woodpecker hole he'd drill into the mast; the frayed cotton of the fuse flustered by the breeze, lifting and flicking until it took the flame. Then a soft hiss. An internal thump. Before brief absolute quiet – the darkest point a moment before dawn – before the roar.

'We should take the blades first,' Mal said. The turbine now in sections, the weather moving in.

———

The brothers worked with deliberate rhythm, with procedure now automatic after three weeks on the hill.

They rivetted the long tarp to a broad edge of one of the halved sections of the turbine mast, then used the rivet gun to punch holes below the other long edge. Into the holes they fed chains. Then they harnessed the chains to the oxen.

The holes made by the rivet gun seemed to bleed, as if from wounds made by a nail.

The rain hit as they loaded the travois, carrying the sections of blade like planks. The rain was percussive, drove suddenly violently into them, as if it wanted to dislodge the two men from the face of the moor.

When they had the sections on the travois, and the heavy solar battery, they moved off with the oxen, the rain mercifully at their back.

─────────

'You would have to count the skulls,' their father said, 'to know.'

A glow of embers sat beneath the griddle rested on two stones from the boundary wall that ringed the part-collapsed house. They had moved in for the time it would take to clear the hill.

Pungent steam came from the pot atop the griddle. The same steam came from the bowls in their hands.

'Many,' Iohan said.

Their spoons against the bowls made the sound of the oxen chain clinking as they drew the blades across the moor.

'Foot and Mouth,' the father said. 'Some farmers burned their herds.'

The weather snapped at the carbon tarp that spanned a collapsed section of the roof, the snap their coats had made earlier, before the front closed in.

It was as if the day's sounds had followed the men back into the room.

'You?'

'No.'

'We didn't know.'

'I was three.'

A ping came from the section of turbine fashioned as a fireplace. A flu that took the smoke away through the low ceiling.

'The piles burned for weeks. Hellish. The smell. Worse than the flex casings.'

Iohan watched the fire. A curl of bracken at its edge, as if pushed out, rejected, glowed faintly with heat, arched, like one of the terrible ribcages in miniature.

'My mother cut my hair the day our neighbours put fire to their herd. I thought it was my cut hair I smelled. Even now I think that.'

'You don't have hair now.'

'Even that did not kill our type of farming.'

The father seemed momentarily to look away, as if there were no walls between him and the outside world.

'Well, the scrap is easier than sheep.'

Mal suddenly saw his father as far lonelier than he knew. He looked down from him, to his own trouser sleeves, wet and stained berry-purple from pushing through the whin.

'When did this happen? This burning.'

'Millennium. Thereabouts.'

They were all quiet for a while.

Mal chewed at the stew. 'Must have been about the time this rabbit was young.'

————

Mal stamped apart the ceiling boards pulled part-rotted from the more derelict rooms above. They had previously piled all burnable material together. A mantlepiece of heavy oak. Picture frames. Brittle gorse.

As lighting splints, they used the desiccated folds of newspaper found rolled and packed against the window seals. The paper gone sepia, the print, in places, chromatogrammed into tiny flowers they thought at first was mould.

The papers were from before the two brothers were born.

Iohan read the news with wonder. Like it was prophecy. Further treasure maps that people must have followed to this future.

'Are you going back out?' the father asked.

'We'll wait.' The ping and crack of the hearth. 'Until the weather has blown over.' But the wind had dropped, and the rain set in.

'The oil should have settled. We'll need diesel soon,' to drive the old truck, to take the loads of metal and glass fibre powder to the dealers. 'I'll get to making that.'

'Then I'll go for the nacelle,' said Iohan. 'I don't mind the rain.'

'Maybe the oxen do.'

He did not say, Iohan, that he felt drawn back by the bones. That he needed to look again at them, now he knew why they were there.

––––––––

The wet air brought the chimney smoke down in a cloak about the outbuildings. They appeared shrouded in mist.

Dismantled sections of the turbines lay organised about the place. The mast sections a stack of strange timber; the blunt nacelles gathered like the product of some quarry.

Mal went across the yard. He braced against a wind no longer present; took some seconds to recognise there was now no chaotic orchestration to the skyborne sounds. Just the structured mathematical patter of the rain.

He went into the smaller outbuilding. They had drained the

lubricating oil and coolant from the nacelles, as if collecting wealth from some strange giant fruit, and he checked now to see the impurities had settled from it. Held the container up to the white oblong of the open doorway.

A band of sediment lay gathered in the base of the container, faint clouds stirring from it with his movement.

The oil at the top of the containers was clear. He could turn this into diesel.

Mal bundled the stripped-off flex casing and cable sheath into the base of the high-heat chamber and lit it with one of the newspaper splints, recoiling from the acrid flare and closing the grate.

———————

The spines and ribs and smaller cast-about bones lay in a mayhem correlant to the procedure that had set them there; but there was a patience to the solid skulls Iohan could not settle with. An accusation they seemed prepared to wait the resolution of.

He had effectively walked out of the rain, as it moved to set in over the higher ground, and the land throbbed with tones after its saturation.

The uncovered earth-ash of the pit was a dark sludge like some stuff of primal reformation.

When Iohan turned from the pit, he saw the oxen were gazing into the eye sockets of the skulls.

It unnerved him such that he felt his heartbeat in his head; and the claustrophobia of the open space; as if the oxen would turn on him.

But then, a far-off rhythm thumping in the air. A sub-sound suggesting some turbine had restored itself and started spinning. That Iohan felt through his body. An insane conviction that such a turbine would approach over the horizon with intent to call him into judgement for his work.

Then the helicopter breached the hill. Battling. The metal box it carried, like some strange outsized prey, swinging dangerously in the wind.

The oxen bridled. The rotors of the helicopter. The sense they came to reclaim the severed blades in family retribution. Thuddered over them. Swallowed and swaying in the wind. Its sound doubling off the moor. Shipping container penduline as the bizarre thing chopped through the sky, away over the bluff.

As Iohan left with the nacelle loaded on the travois, one of the standing turbines span just once, a graunching cry, as if in lament for its dereliction. Or that it called out plaintive for the helicopter to return.

———————

The next day an actual mist sat loose and shifting thickly on the moor, so it was not possible to go out to the turbines.

Instead, the brothers cut the blades up in the shallow they had excavated for this purpose, some fifty metres square. They had scalped out the shallow with the ox-drawn scraper.

With the air still and thickened, a faint smell of fish reached them from the protein lake beyond the distant ridge.

The oxen steamed as they circled, appearing to clear a ring amongst the mist, their hooves sucking in the churned ground as they drew water from the tarn into the sprayers and the spray went out to dampen down the dust.

Even with this spray, the cut glass fibre lifted in motes about the brothers. Fell into pastes about the cut blades, slathered and hurried to take new form. Settled upon the peat.

The pieces of the blades fell into parts like bits of bone, and neither brother talked of it.

'That krill stinks,' Mal complained.

———————

During the afternoon the air cleared, and the weather moved away. Three helicopters came, two with containers and one with some immense machine.

'Perhaps they'll take the metal,' Mal suggested. 'If they're going back and forth.'

The scale of the moor, after the mist, seemed to have grown. The ridge beyond which the helicopters had gone more distant than before.

'Where are they coming from?' Iohan asked.

'They'll be houses,' said their father. 'Relocators.'

'Before they flood the valley?'

'I do not think those people would live in a group. They are farmers, mostly. They wouldn't want to live in a group.'

They looked up and out across the hill.

'They'll be from somewhere on the coast.'

———————

When he stabled the oxen that night, their slap and snort, the rough rasp of their breath, Iohan, he was certain, heard laughter and the sound of work coming softened – made spectral in some way – across the dark moor.

Every now and then came the strange whirring call of nightjars.

He took the hand-crank torch and a bottle of fir spirit and walked the distance to the ridge.

The night was deeply clear.

The flank of the facing hillside was busy with fireflies of light. Blinking points even brighter than the pools of solarflood in which they sat. With the magnesium-bright flash of welding torches; a distant sing of plasma cutters.

The smell of krill was thick again, in the night air. An otherworldly glow, the plankton phosphorescent, a thin steam upon the heated lake below.

Iohan could see the containers being manoeuvred into place. Stacked and windows cut into them. The colours stony in the clean white light.

He thought of the bones in the pit, and the broken teeth of the turbine bases, and of moving on again. The nightjars, whirr. Of the quiet, patient dynamite.

Behind him, the night pooled in the dip of the moor, like some great body of dark water.

'Father is right,' he thought. 'There are people coming here to live.'

'Oxen' was originally drafted during work for the BBC Radio 4 commission Stillicide (Granta Books, 2019)

Fordlandia

Sophie Shillito

The trees bear the scars, still. Calloused remembrance ribbons spiral round the trunks. Long claw marks scratch across their skin, where curved knives bled milk for rubber tyres and gaskets, valves and hose. Sliced grooves wept until the catching cups overflowed, and creamy sap spoiled in the heavy jungle air, curdling the dream.

A ship slid up the wide, brown river, packed with things for a new life. Doorknobs. A piano for the clubhouse. Sealing wax. An ice machine and a walnut bureau. Iron bedsteads for the hospital and a polished wooden floor to dance on. Needles for the tailor, books for the library, stethoscopes and a franking machine. Crates of canned beans, metal tins of hair cream. Spoons, saucepans, carbolic soap and carpets, school uniforms and slippers, a water tower painted engine silver. Sacks stuffed with pride and a chest full of conceit.

Executives in broad-brimmed hats waded ashore through moonlit shallows, seeking their fortunes. They ordered their men to burn the jungle and chop a clearing at the bottom of the mountain. The men fanned the red fire tiger, and grubbed out woody stumps, tearing at the forest with axes and anger until the land was wounded and tamed, and all that was left was an earthen plateau, strewn with leaves and memory.

A village grew – rows of clapboard bungalows, as white as the teeth of the crocodiles that crawled out of the river. Picket fences striped round the edges of plots; on street corners, fire hydrants pimpled from baked concrete. Just like home. Smiling children played hoop and ran in to wash hands for dinner, neat and nice.

In the mornings, the chiefs left their white lace wives in starched, swept homes, and walked through shaded lanes to chide the men working on the plantation. In the heat of the day, screen doors clicked shut, thwarting snakes that curled across freshly painted window sills, narrowing their eyes at golden babies in their cribs and winding away into gutters. At night, couples sat in wicker hoop chairs, on verandas, looking at the sky. Everything was moist.

The sun brooded over the river, carving through ripples and eddies. Heat brought things up from the deep, to a rolling boil on the surface. Slippery wet with sweat, the men set out into the forest, propping ladders against trunks, slicing their fury and sadness out of the trees, staining the oppressive, simmering afternoons with sap as sticky as blood.

Tempers frayed at the edges, fists were raised. Sick to the stomach of brown rice and tinned peaches, the men tore up the canteen, chopping the chairs with shining machetes and hacking the legs off tables. A mosaic of shattered plates crunched underfoot as they chased the executives back to the ship. Riverside dreams were drowned on the shore.

Vehicles with no place to go rust in the old workshop. Outside, a buckled sign hangs from a broken bracket – faded words whisper *Ford Motor Company*. Sunlight falls on the corrugated metal roof, making it tick. Mosquitoes skate on puddles in the dented asphalt road that reflect the broken windows of the warehouse.

Paint peels off the hotel and the restaurant menu is stale. The letters on the monument fall from their nails, making new words in the dirt. Dust from spalling brickwork coats the church pulpit. In the cemetery, crosses lie on their sides, marking the place the dead are buried.

Mould blooms on the wall of the classroom and speckles over the school books, as green shoots sprout through the wooden floor and rats run underneath. The swings in the playground blow in the breeze, squealing like children.

Manicured lawns grow long and unkempt. Tendrils coil in through the roofs of the houses. Hairy spiders and leaf ants scribble messages in abandoned diaries; mealy mites and fat caterpillars burrow through unmade beds.

Wild vines stick their tongues through the doors of the hospital – slinking through the laboratories, weeding in through the pharmacy windows. Spores blind the eye chart in the optician's office and decay rots the dentist's chair. Bats make a roost in the ceiling of the operating theatre, flapping and shrieking. The jungle has wound its way home. Tacked to the wall of the X-ray room are the shadows of people who knew this place. The past shows itself like fractured bone, splintering through time.

At the jetty, chains drag and tangle. Posts unmoored from their fixings scatter over the silted shore. The river moves sluggishly, wearing an oilskin jacket, brushing alluvium over the corpse of a water bird. It sluices dirty sediment through the husk of an upturned car and makes a raft of a rubber tyre. Ribcage roots of mangroves grip the bank, holding back jungle lungs filled with old, sodden soil.

Bears with Lawyers

Shaun Tan

Bears with lawyers.

It was as simple and terrible as that.

For the first time in a very long while, longer than anyone could remember, or wanted to remember, the bears were able to speak through legal representatives: men and women in black gowns who studied Ursine and held aloft the hefty paperwork that allowed their clients to walk freely through the city without being shot. And walk they did, right past armed police and animal-control officers, past bewildered motorists and pedestrians, workers and shoppers, right into our great halls of justice.

Humankind was being sued, it turned out. A class action of epic proportions: *Ursidae vs Homo sapiens*.

That wasn't the worst of it.

Human Law is not the only legal system on the planet, it turned out. There are as many systems as there are species, the lawyers for the bears explained to an incredulous room, under which all animals are recognised as legal entities within a cosmic hierarchy. Human Law isn't even very high on this hierarchy (apparently we are just below Walrus Law) and Bear Law actually takes precedence in most cases. The fact that we didn't know any of this only seemed to strengthen the bears' case at the expense of our own.

Shaken? Yes, but hardly worried, and we are not ones to flinch. We had the best legal team that money could buy and immediately launched our broadside. *We do not recognise so-called Bear Law! No such nonsense has ever existed! You have nothing to show us!*

And so the bears showed us.

Sure enough, there it was as plain as day, in all places we never bothered to look: on the tailfins of freshwater trout, under the bark of trees, in the creased silt of riverbeds, on the wing-scale of moths and butterflies, in the cursive coastlines of entire continents. Moss, sand, dew, the arrangement of seeds in a berry, pollen, bacteria, everything. Put a single slice of any rock under the right light and it is all there, literally written in stone. It was humbling, beautiful and indisputable and horrifying. It was all those things. Especially for a legal team that had spent their entire working life in a city, who knew nothing more than the contents of human filing cabinets and libraries. Which were only ever written by humans, it turned out. And meant very little to the rest of the world, it turned out.

That wasn't the worst of it.

Lawyers for the bears now presented us with all the translated paperwork we had requested, stacks of it in huge boxes, boxes that filled shipping containers, shipping containers that sat on the back of trucks, trucks lined up in a convoy, as far as the eye could see. The city's traffic ground to a halt as they backed one by one into the streets of our brightest legal firms, every fluorescent light and mahogany veneer trembling. If that sight was not demoralising enough, reading any fraction of the material, a case against humankind gathered over some ten thousand years, was an exercise in abject despair. *Theft. Pillage. Unlawful Occupation. Deportation. Slavery. Murder. Torture. Genocide.* Not to mention all the crimes we'd never even heard of like *Spiritual Exclusion, Groaking* and *Ungungunurumunre.*

'For the hungriest of all animals,' said the bears in their typically abstruse legal verse, 'the only thing left to eat is the truth.' As if to prove their point, none of our lawyers could view the supporting library video of evidence without losing their lunch.

We countersued, appealed, sought injunctions, mined every technicality and loophole, hiring and firing our own lawyers like there was no tomorrow. We were trumped each time, the bears always sitting so silent and resolute in the upper gallery. How we came to detest their calm, round shapes and sad black eyes. The extent to which we loathed their lawyers we could not even begin to express. Who were these people? They turned our every argument against us, each time presenting some precedent of Bear Law as old and unbreakable as time, dragging various bits of primeval forest into the courtroom. Again and again they exposed the shallowness of every Human Law as presumption, ignorance and hubris.

That wasn't the worst of it.

Deep in our hearts we knew they were right. Even as we fought our defence with such intellectual ferocity, as if to convince ourselves more than our opponents of a truth mired in self-contradiction, we knew the end was coming. It was time to reach a settlement. We called in every favour and came up with a figure that made our eyes water and our mouths dry, a figure too staggering to ever make public.

'Your money is meaningless to us,' said the bears. 'You grasp economics with the same clawless paws you use for fumbling justice.'

And, once again, the bears showed us.

There they were, God help us, the Ledgers of the Earth, written in clouds and glaciers and sediments, tallied in the colours of the sun and the moon as light passed through the millennial sap of every living thing, and we looked upon it all with dread. Ours was not the only fiscal system in the world, it turned out. And worse, our debt was severe beyond reckoning. And worse than worse, all the capital we had accrued throughout history was a collective figment of the human imagination: every asset, stock and dollar. We owned nothing. The bears asked us to relinquish our hold on all that never belonged to us in the first place.

Well, this we simply could not do.

So we shot the bears.

All perfectly legal, it turned out, thanks to a bill passed in the dead of night. We took care of their lawyers too, in a manner we are not at liberty to divulge. But we did ask them, before they went, 'Why on earth did you do it? How could you, yourselves human beings, with homes and families and communities, represent those bears, speak for them, support litigation against your own species?'

'We had no choice,' they said. 'We are sworn to uphold justice.'

Oh, please. Humans always have a choice: is that not what makes us unique? And is silence not a form of peace? We'll never understand why it is so difficult for some people to accept the hard truth of the world. Why they fight, even when they know they cannot win.

And so, finally, finally, finally, things went back to normal.

Until now.

Until now, when the whole sorry and sordid experience with those damned bears comes flooding back. Blood is leeching from every face in the boardroom, and we can already hear the sound of document trucks reversing into streets. A fetid cloud descends over the city, the sickening stench of endless torment and persecution.

'The cattle are here,' a terrified receptionist quavers over the intercom, 'with lawyers.'

Shaun Tan
Bears with Lawyers, Oil on canvas

Effie Paleologou
Nest #1, Colour print on Hahnemühle Photo Rag, 2019
An abandoned blackbird's nest fully deconstructed,
its 921 sticks arranged in a formal linear way.

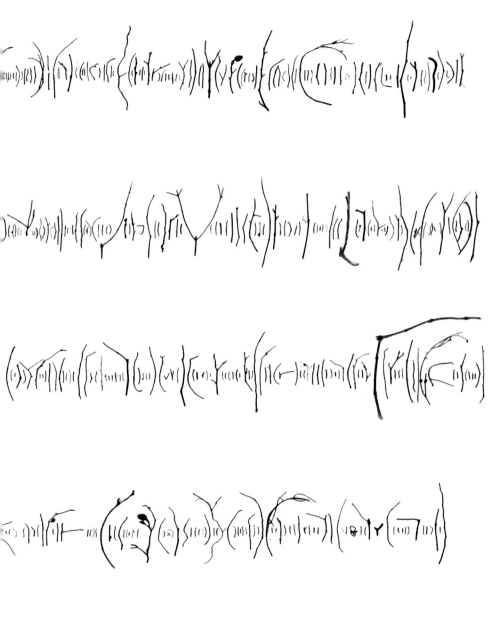

Sarah Ainslie
At Purfleet's Estuary, Photomontage, 2020

Sunandini Banerjee
Desert Sky, 1, Digital Collage

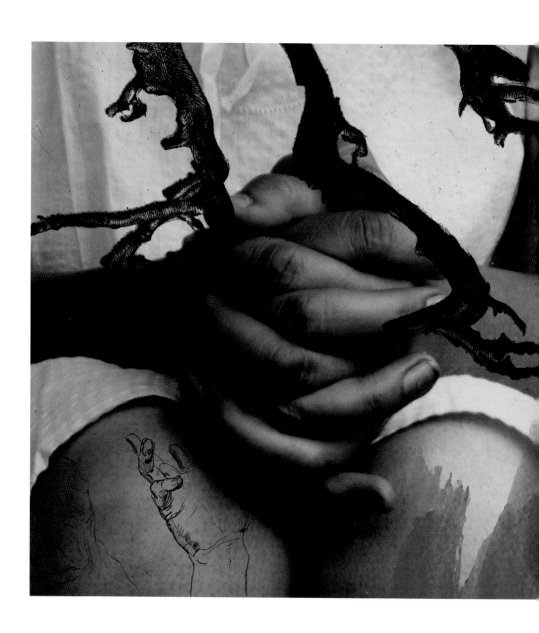

Sunandini Banerjee
Clasp, Digital collage

Jon Jost
The Berkeley Pit, Photo collage, 2015

The Berkeley Pit is the site of the biggest superfund clean up in the United States. In 2012, I began photographing it, playing with these shots, making collages of them – expressive of the Pit, and strangely extracting beauty from the devastation these photos represent – one of the ironies of art. The layered terraces dig deeper into the earth, telling a story both geological, technological and human. Buried in the rubble are the stories of Butte and its miners, drawn from around the globe. Most of those stories, like the vast majority of stories, are never told.

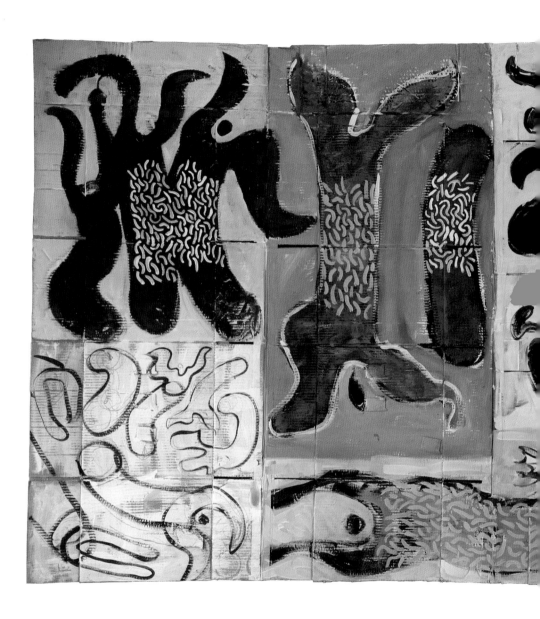

John Weeden
Seven Generations, Gouache on cardboard, 2020

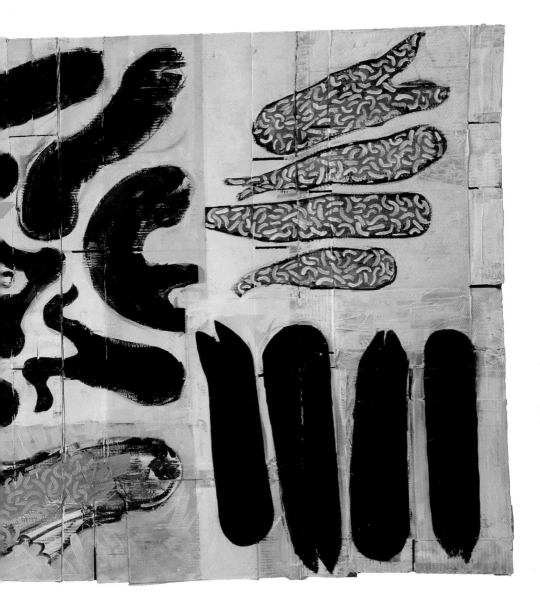

Luisa-Maria MacCormack
The Great Beast,
Pastel on paper, 2019

'And the Beast which I saw' is a series of works that takes its inspiration from a variety of apparently incongruous sources: the bacchanalian scenes of excess so ubiquitous to Baroque era art, antique 'erotica' of the seventeenth century, Assyrian relief sculpture and our own era of extreme and catastrophic consumption. Considerations about climate change, the ravaged natural world and the fast disappearing 'ethnosphere' are questions never far from the minds of our generation. These works act as an allegory for our current state of being – a species lost to its own hedonistic self-absorption, sleepwalking to the edge of an irretrievable precipice.

William Bock
from his Rewilders series: *Rewilder II Andrew*, Cape Clear, Ireland, Photograph, 2018
[opposite] *Rewilder IV Isatu*, Lough Hyne, Ireland, Photograph, 2020

The Rewilders is an ongoing series of photographic portraits of people created using wild plants and materials found in specific natural environments. The portraits celebrate the untamed and uncertain borders between human and plant life, merging the unique qualities of a given landscape with the human beings that inhabit it.

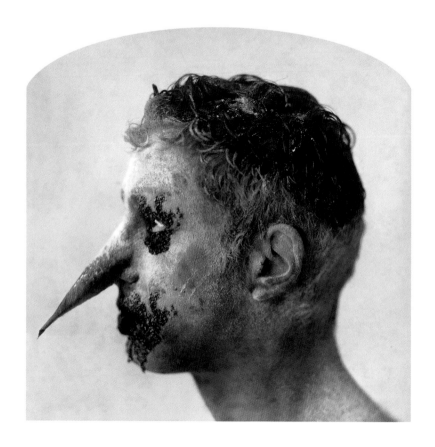

Kahn & Selesnick
The Thieving Magpie

The Thieving Magpie

Kahn & Selesnick

At a certain point, it had become evident that life was never going to return to normal, or at least not to the way it had been before. Perhaps it was this realisation that caused the eruption of spontaneous theatrical happenings in unlikely locations throughout the city, usually the more bizarre and extravagant the better and preferably apocalyptic in flavour. Predictably, Orlofsky could not have been more delighted by these spectacles; I would arrive at his rooms and we would set out through the greying streets, following a seemingly random trajectory, yet somehow always managing to coincide with at least one impromptu masquerade somewhere over the course of our rambles. Some memorable scenes: a gloomy twilight at Paddington, full of weary commuters who suddenly all performed a highly synchronised dance routine, briefcases and raincoats aswirl like dervishes, feverish yet deeply melancholy; a flash-dinner on the district line, the table and chairs hastily installed at Earl's Court, the wait staff and food at South Kensington, the diners at Victoria, all five courses consumed by Canon Street, any trace of the event removed at Tower Hill, by which time we had long since missed our disembarkation at Embankment; or perhaps most memorably, a bus full of passengers, both upstairs and down, wearing rubber animal masks, their heads all facing forwards in uniform resignation as the bus disappeared into the rainy mists of Little Rupert Street. I would return to the rooms agitated and exhausted by encounters with ticket collectors dressed as penguins, guerrilla pastry chefs, financiers erupting into plainsong, or tramps reciting Beowulf.

Eventually, at least so it seemed to me, this extravagant mummery seemed to extend to every single exchange or encounter, no matter how trivial or unimportant, as if life itself were asterixed with a disclaimer saying that all participants acknowledged this was merely a performance, that all roles were temporary and subject to change at any time. This might seem to suggest that the city had been overcome with a kind of Borgesian infection in which the theatrical event and real life come to resemble each other more and more closely until they are identical in every way, but I felt that the opposite was the case, that we were falling into a rapidly diverging mass delusion, strained to breaking point. Winks, secret handshakes, strange gestures, florid and ridiculous turns of phrase, unusual hats: it was as if every single person had become a freemason almost overnight, initiated into some kind of arcane and secret knowledge. I remember sitting with Orlofsky eating Hamburg sandwiches in a café in the shopping precinct, our conversation constantly interrupted (a head tap and grimace exchanged with a man seated at the opposite table) by a stream of (a wink and a hoot with a woman cleaning the table) tics and gesticulations (a flapping motion with a man holding an empty birdcage), and wondering what it meant when everyone is initiated; perhaps the aims of the great enlightenment had finally been realised, *liberté, égalité,* and *fraternité* for all, a theatre of perfect integration and harmony, despite the deterioration of a world collapsing about our ears. Orlofsky had got up, given me a normal handshake, and departed; as soon as he was gone, the knowing glances all subsided, the stares became blank and disinterested, no one passed by the plated glass dressed as a dancing bear, rubbish blown down the avenues became just that, depressing and dingy. It was as if he were the sole audience member of this weird parade, and it dawned on me that perhaps only Orlofsky was initiated into the arcane secrets of the world, the rest of us merely actors within his memory palace, sad and beautiful and absurd.

Ghost Frogs

Bridget Pitt

There is a town, let's call it Williams Bay, although you could substitute any white Anglo-Saxon man's name. Such names still haunt this African country, cluttering up the place like old armoured tanks – rusting and redundant, like the faded pennants of conquerors who refuse to die. Or perhaps serving as reminders that, despite the trappings of self-governance, this nation is still painfully in thrall to the white men across the sea.

We could also call it let's-demolish-all-natural-beauty-for-the-sake-of-industry-bay. Which would be more descriptive although unwieldy on the tongue.

The town has a long narrow beach stitched along on its eastern flank. This is defended by a strip of dark entangled forest, home to wild animals, murderers, thieves, and all manners of strangeness (according to Grandma Whitaker). The waves are violent, with treacherous tides, and the beach is mostly shunned by the townsfolk. The town is thus hunched against its shoreline, choosing to focus its compound smoky eyes on its famous bay – a broad scoop of water biting deep into the shore. The bay is imposed on by several seemingly random piers resting on dolosse – hefty concrete bicuspids designed to defeat the rising ocean's efforts to claim the land. (*Dolos*, the Afrikaans word for a knuckle bone, is a bone commonly thrown by sangomas to interpret messages from the ancestors. It's unclear what message these dollosse bring, but there are so many in this town you can only conclude that they're breeding.)

The forefathers could do little to tame the beach, but the bay has been rigorously, irredeemably colonised, with one third in the steel-and-concrete grip of a vast industrial harbour. It was commandeered in the nineteenth century by the British to help ferry coal gouged from South African hillsides across the ocean – a purpose it serves diligently to this day.

Walking to the shunned beach one Thursday afternoon in late summer is an assemblage, a holobiont or an ecosystem, who goes by the name of Skye. Fewer than half of Skye's cells have the DNA of a human, and one of the forty-six chromosomes in each of these cells is that extra X chromosome which denotes Skye's body as female in our classification-obsessed society.

But Skye resists the binary nature of such definitions, the this-or-thatness, the sheep-or-goatness of it. There are many moments when they feel more like a tadpole or a tree than a human, never mind a human as specific as a boy or a girl. They are both and neither, they are energy and empty space, they are a confusion of longings, an amalgam of rages and sorrows, threaded with quicksilver flashes of delight. What has all this got to do with their reproductive organs? Among friends Skye refers to themselves as they, not only because it is gender neutral but also because its suggested plurality pleases them. They've always thought of themselves as *we* or *us*, and were excited to discover that they were a biological community rather than a singularity. It helped to account for their persistent sensation of being more-than-one.

But they're not among friends in Williams Bay, and have yet to meet anyone in this town who might grasp the idea of a gender-neutral pronoun. Here, Skye is a 'she', but then again, here they're so invisible, or visible in the wrong way – that way of being visible when people don't know what box to put you in so you sit outside their boxes and vex them – that pronouns are just one of many small acts of violence that the town imposes on them.

Skye makes their daily trek to the beach on a path through the wicked forest, in defiance of their now departed Grandma, with only dead-Grandma's dog to protect them. Topsy is a ratty little thing of uncertain breed. She's unlikely to deter any but the most timid assailant – notwithstanding her fixed demonic grin, legacy of a broken jaw from her efforts to bite the wheels of passing cars. But Skye has developed a certain recklessness since concluding that they, like all humans, dwell in the shadow of some imminent anthropogenically induced doom. Besides, they have to get to the beach because they have a task to complete, a Sisyphean labour they've set themselves to punish them for being human. And that task is picking up nurdles.

There are thousands of nurdles to be picked up, on this beach alone. These tiny plastic nuggets resemble seeds. But they'll never grow anything but the plethora of plasticky things they're melted down to create. Each year, some two hundred thousand tons get into the sea, by falling off ships, or being washed down drains. Which is an inconceivably massive quantity of nurdles. South African seas got an extra deluge recently, when a violent unseasonal storm tipped a container of two billion into Durban harbour.

Birds and turtles think that nurdles are food. They're not.

They're worse than not-food. Because they draw to themselves all the other toxins and sadness that humans have thrown into the ocean. Skye's read about an albatross that was found with a hundred nurdles and other plastic in its stomach.

It will come as no surprise to anyone that the bird was dead.

The violent unseasonal storm was one of a growing number of violent unseasonal things that happen when people fuck with the climate by burning fossil fuels. But Skye is not going to think about *that* now.

They're cultivating the art of not thinking, because thinking often makes them sad. This may be because there is much to be sad about, or it may be because the microbes in their gut are out of balance. Or so Skye has read, in an email from their mother. Their mother's way of dealing with their sometimes crippling sorrow is to send helpful articles on how to cultivate cheer – apparently one way is by placating one's gut microbes with probiotics and sauerkraut. Skye doesn't like sauerkraut, and the money they get from waiting tables at the Pizza Palace doesn't cover probiotics . Their mother didn't seem to consider this when offering this advice. She'd probably send the money if asked, but Skye's not going to do *that*.

Skye pauses to consult their microbes on their state of balance. It's hard to hear your own stomach, because you can't put your ear on it. Skye recalls how a boy they once loved would lay his head on their stomach and say he could hear it singing to him, like a whale in the ocean. Or perhaps a bird, he'd say, because I can also hear chirping. Skye listens now, but can hear neither whales nor birds nor microbes, only the roar of the waves on the beach and a distant keening of seagulls. They don't shout about it, but Skye thinks their microbes probably are distressed. A diet of pizza and Coke Zero is unlikely to keep them happy.

Skye gives up on their microbes, and carries on walking to the point they left off yesterday, marked by a tree washed ashore during the same unseasonal storm that upended the nurdles. They crouch down on the sand, and pick up the larger bits of litter within reach (four water bottles, three soda bottles, one mayonnaise jar, half a comb, three lids, some unidentifiable plastic shreds, a hair curler, five ear buds, a cigarette lighter, and ten cigarette butts). Then begin sifting the sand with a rusty wire sieve from Grandma's kitchen, to get the nurdles. It's easy to imagine why a fish might think they're food because they look like little bits of shell, or small non-pearlescent pearls. Something a chronically despondent oyster might produce. Skye is collecting them in a plastic tub that once contained ice cream, which they carry in a plastic shopping bag. Both of these things were probably birthed by nurdles. It takes one to catch one.

They have been collecting them daily for three weeks now, enough to fill about six ice cream containers, but every day the sea brings more. Sometimes, in the evening, they sit and sift their hands through them, wondering at their persistence and plasticity. They wonder about all the plastic particles they themselves have inadvertently ingested, picture them swimming about their secret inner seas and choking their microbial companions. Each night they walk the beach again, through dreams littered with plastic.

There is something compelling and meditative, even soothing, about sifting for nurdles, if you turn you brain off from contemplating how many there are and how many things they kill. Skye is soon so absorbed in not thinking and sieving nurdles that they don't notice that they're no longer alone, until a voice breaks through the muffling roar of the ocean.

'Plenty more where that comes from.'

Skye starts and looks up, seeing first a pair of pale feet in grubby orange crocs then solid reddish legs downed with blond hair, rumpled blue shorts, a white T-shirt which declares that *Donuts are just Gay Bagels* (a statement which seems intended to offend someone, although whether its gays, donuts or bagels is hard to tell.) Above the T-shirt is a sun reddened face under short colourless hair, with squinty eyes over a self-congratulatory smirk, as if its owner just said something uncommonly witty. He's standing too close – Skye can smell sun cream, beer, cigarettes, sweat. They want to stand up too, to face him on his level, but they don't want to give him that acknowledgement. So they just drop their eyes and shuffle a few feet down the beach, then carry on sifting through the sand.

'How you gonna do it?' Orange Croc Man demands with some belligerence, and a small kick of a sand-filled chip packet that they haven't yet gathered. 'There's trash everywhere. All the way from here to Cape Town, tons of the stuff, how you gonna pick up all that trash, huh?'

Skye stares at the grubby toes, visible through the holes in the orange dome of the croc. What a monumentally ugly sight, that foot, that shoe, that obscure grievance beaming down on them. Is he annoyed that they're picking up trash at all, or annoyed that they won't pick up all of it?

'Piles of trash,' he reiterates. The crocs have carried his feet down the beach so that he's standing above Skye again. Perhaps they too are drawn by the nurdle containers. 'Bottles, packets, all sorts. You can't believe what people chuck out. Fridges. Dead dogs. Once I found a couch, for Chris' sake. Ya, ya, none so queer as folks, eh?' This last in a conspiratorial tone, as if he'd decided abruptly to join their cause.

Skye says not a word, does not look up, carries on methodically sieving the sand for nurdles. Why is this person still here? Surely he will go, any minute? But he doesn't.

'Sorry, I should've introduced myself. I'm Brian,' he says. And, as if this declaration has granted him an invitation, he flops down on the sand.

Topsy, the evil creature, doesn't nip his ankles as she usually does to strangers. Instead she furiously wags her little grey backside, and licks his hand. He laughs, and rubs her head in a way that looks profoundly annoying to Skye, but Topsy doesn't bite his fingers.

'What's your name?'

Skye ignores him.

'Where you from?'

Skye ignores him.

'Do you speak English? Are you from Germany? There was a chick I once met from Germany, she looked a bit like you...'

Skye ignores him.

'Are you deaf?' he asks, louder, but without much malice or accusation, more as if he's finally hit on a good explanation for their lack of response. Skye reluctantly sits back on their haunches. Clearly Brian needs more frankness in his messaging.

'No, I'm not deaf. I just like my own company, no offence.'

[136]

Brian nods. Then waves his hand to take in the beach. 'So...Ja, well... like I said, lot of trash. You could use some help, methinks. What's that?'

He is pointing to the tattoo on their chest, just above the T-shirt line. 'We are all ghosts' he reads, enunciating each word carefully. He laughs. 'That's funny. Do you believe in ghosts? I don't. My mom does, but she... you know...' he tips his head back and raises his hand, to mimic drinking from a bottle. 'What's the picture? Is it supposed to be a ghost? Because it actually looks like a frog, methinks.'

Skye raises their hand to cover the words, and the image beneath it.

'It's a ghost frog,' they mumble. They've never regretted getting the tattoo, but they do regret the way it seems to give a certain kind of person licence to interrogate their body.

He laughs, as if they'd made a joke. 'Ghost frog' he chuckles.

Skye keeps their hand on the tattoo, to shield it from his gaze. They imagine they can feel the slight pulsing breath of the ghost frog under their fingers. The Table Mountain ghost frog is a small jewel of a creature, green or brown with purple blobs as if it had been playing miniature paintball with blueberries. Its eyes are perfectly round speckled pebbles, transected from top to bottom by a vertical diamond-shaped black pupil. It's about the length of the palm of your hand, and is almost flat so that it can squeeze under rocks. Its fingers and toes have little suckers on them to help it cling to slippery surfaces. The tadpoles have mouths that can anchor them to water weed on rocks in fast flowing streams.

Table Mountain Ghost Frogs are very specific about where they live. They have a habitat that is only about ten square kilometres, and live only in the perennial streams rushing down Table Mountain. They have been birthed by these streams, and seem to have birthed them in turn. They birthed each other, as if a part of the stream one day decided to hop out of the water and sing to the mossy rocks, and this song in turn manifested the stream to flow more deeply and swiftly. Their song is a musical warble punctuated with short notes, like water both flowing and dripping. They are called Ghost frogs, it's thought, because they were first spotted in Skeleton Gorge on Table Mountain.

Nowadays, as global warming dries their streams, their name has a crueller meaning.

Skye stares past their awkward, unwanted visitor to the unbroken line of rubbish stretching into the distance. They recall the signs they used to see in natural parks on childhood visits to these places. The signs said, 'leave only footprints, take only photographs'. Skye remembers feeling virtuous and happy because they were a light-stepping harmless creature who left only footprints and didn't even take photographs as they didn't have a camera. That was before they realised that humans never leave only footprints, at least not since they started domesticating other beings.

Humans are sad, clumsy violent things. They are everything ghost frogs are not.

Except that now, they too, are ghosts.

This is the testimony and rationale of Skye's tattoo. But Skye never explains it, and says nothing to Brian now.

Brian is still chuckling, but Skye can feel him peering at them expectantly, as if waiting for some elucidation of this joke of a frog that is also a ghost. At length he realises that nothing more will be said, and starts half-heartedly shuffling plastic bits that aren't nurdles into the ice-cream carton instead of the bag. Skye watches, disturbed by the breach of protocol. They want to say something, but when he lifts his muddy gaze to theirs, Skye spots some naked vulnerability in his eyes. He is a misfit, an oddity, and Skye sees, in the instant before they turn away, some flicker of his dismal life – the schoolyard bully-ing, the dreary dwelling shared with his ghost-spotting boozy mother, lonely as fuck. His T-shirt is not, perhaps, designed to offend, but some pitiful effort at camouflage, so that he blends in with all the dickheads in William's Bay and doesn't attract dangerous attention.

If he were a dog, Skye would befriend him. But lonely humans are a grim liability. Especially ones as insistent as Brian. His solid, furry legs flop outwards onto the sand, as if he doesn't know where to put them.

'I used to study ghost frogs. For my master's thesis.' Skye offers this small titbit impulsively, as some kind of apology for being so flayed by his need, and instantly regrets it. But Brian has no idea what hangs on that simple statement. Not least the resolution that Skye had made that they would never tell anyone in Williams Bay about ghost frogs. Nor about their succumbing to a savage, crippling grief, as they realised the futility of charting the ghost frogs' steady decline, the futility of trying to sustain any life and hope on a planet that was being suffocated beneath their feet. Or about the night they'd sat up with a bottle of sleeping pills, trying to think up good reasons not to take them.

At around four am, just about the time that they'd run out of reasons, their dad had phoned to say that Grandma Whitaker had died. Their dad rarely called, and it was so odd, that he should phone at that hour about a death that was not unexpected and would not be much mourned. But the call had saved them from the pills, on that night at least, and Skye sometimes wondered whether the spirit of their Grandma had lurched out of her body and impelled their father to make the call. Grandma was not known for gestures of affection, but she had expressed a certain gruff fondness for Skye on her occasional visits, and didn't care that their hair was short and they never wore dresses.

'I was a tomboy myself,' Gruff Grandma liked to say.

Skye didn't take the pills, although the grief remained, only mildly distracted by Grandma's departure. Instead, they'd tattooed their chest, as some kind of pledge to the frogs they'd forsaken, come to this little coal-obsessed carbuncle of a town for the funeral, and continued to live in Grandma's house. It seemed a fitting punishment for lacking the courage to end their life.

Brian expresses no further curiosity about ghost frogs, and is speaking instead about the ghosts his mother sees, which are all the mangled corpses of people who have been murdered in Williams Bay.

Their souls can't rest, he says, until their murderers meet their just deserts. 'But there's no death penalty now, so *that* won't happen methinks... I'll tell you for nothing, if it was left to me, I'd hang the lot of them, instead of giving them a cushy life in jail.'

I'll tell you for nothing... what a strange choice of phrase. As if everything he had said already hadn't been for nothing. Less than nothing. In fact, Skye would give him almost anything now to stop him talking. They keep moving down the beach, but he shuffles after them, picking up a few bits of plastic but mostly just issuing a torrent of free yet unwanted words, describing with some relish each murder victim who has haunted his mother. Until Skye begins to wonder if he is quite so harmless after all, if these stories are some kind of gruesome warning. If he himself dispatched these people into ghostliness, and trawls the beach looking for fresh prey.

'Here's a good one,' he says, brandishing an old aerosol canister of insecticide. The word *Doom* is still faintly legible on the label.

What does he mean, *a good one*? Skye watches him stuff the can into their bag. Somehow, this, more than anything, strikes them as an act of intolerable intrusion. They find the resolve at last to leap to their feet, and snatch up the bag, the sieve and the ice-cream container.

'Sorry, I have to go,' they mumble, and turn to walk rapidly away.

'Hey, is that all the thanks I get?' His wheedling voice pursues them, like a thin hook cast out to snare an escaping fish, only just audible above the crashing of the waves.

'Thanks very much,' Skye throws out, over their shoulder. Topsy is still sitting beside him – she always was a poor judge of character. Skye whistles to her, and carries on walking. They are being rude. But is rudeness the worst you can do? How much of their soul have they given away, their jaw aching with some fixed and terrible smile behind which they died a slow death, just to avoid being rude?

'I'll see you tomorrow,' he calls, or perhaps he doesn't, they wouldn't be able to hear him now above the waves, would they? Perhaps this statement was conjured by their own paranoia, their fear that this Brian had somehow slid through the cracks in their armour to contaminate their existence, and would never again depart.

Skye hurries on, walking as fast as they can without actually running, glancing back only once to see if he is following. He is a distant lump, barely discernible against the sand, only his orange crocs flaring like beacons. Skye walks until even the crocs have faded from view, then drops their packets and runs into the ocean fully clothed, and allows the hard pounding of the waves to exorcise the soft violence of Brian's need and insinuations. They walk away more calmly, shivering in their wet clothes, for a cool breeze is coming off the ocean. They hesitate at the mouth of the forest, and glance back, but he is nowhere in sight. They step onto the path and walk through the entangled trees that lean over them in a way that might seem menacing, although Skye has never been menaced by trees. They fight the urge to run, as their ears strain for the squeaky press of croc rubber on the path behind them.

In the parking lot on the far side of the forest they find a black rubbish bin, with a monkey-proof lid designed to confound the black-faced vervets that overrun Williams Bay. They've never discarded the plastic they've gathered from the beach – they've taken every scrap and nurdle home to Grandma's house. But now they pause, lift the lid of the rubbish bin, take the Doom canister out of their bag and drop it, carefully as if it might explode, onto the assorted detritus in the bin. They look at it lying there for a few seconds, then gently replace the lid, clicking the monkey-proof lock.

Later Skye sits in Grandma's house, nursing a cup of black coffee and contemplating the day's haul of plastic waste. Grandma's house is impossibly brown – the walls are mud coloured, the ceilings nicotine-stained knotted pine. The doors are fake teak, the rooms choked with dark wood cupboards and dressers. The carpets had been the colour of cobwebs, but Skye hauled them to the town dump because they seemed to be knotted with the dust of Grandma's abiding disappoint-ments. They can hear Topsy clipping about the bare floors with an unsettling scratching of claws on wood. Like nails scraping a coffin. She often walks around like that, Topsy, perhaps searching for her old familiar.

Skye has repurposed the dining room for the storage of plastic trash – they have no intentions to host dinner parties. They have no clear plan for the trash, had only felt that it was wrong to throw it away or even to recycle it, because everyone knows most of your recycling ends up in the waste stream. But still. They felt so light after dropping that Doom can in the bin. They'd even skipped a few metres down the road, with Topsy yapping and nipping at their ankles. We couldn't bring it home, now, could we Topsy? Skye says. We don't need any more doom in this household.

They glance through the door to the discarded plastic, carefully sorted in piles on the dining room floor and table. They've had vague thoughts about an artwork, about documenting it on Instagram, about dumping it in the foyers of the companies that created or distributed it but did nothing to get it out of the ocean. But there was already so much of it, and it was so ugly and irredeemable. If we all had to keep our discarded plastic, they tell Topsy, we'd be a lot more circumspect about what we consume.

They wonder about Brian, whether he was still sitting where they left him in his orange crocs, or had found someone else to torment. Walking away from Brian had been almost as liberating as walking away from the doom. But he was right about one thing. When he said *you could use some help, methinks.*

'He's right, Topsy, we really could use some help.'

Skye stares out of the window, thinking about help, where it might be found, and how hard it was to ask for it. They look out onto the Grandma's small back garden, which has been taken over by a sprawling Delicious Monster and a defiant crowd of dandelions. They could take out the monster, Skye thinks. And plant some vegetables. That would make their microbes happier.

Even ghosts need vegetables.

Just having this thought, even if it never happened, felt like a step away from ghostliness.

Skye glances down at Topsy, who has now jumped onto the bench opposite and is peering at them across the table with bright inquisitive eyes, just like Grandma used to.

We know you're in there, Grandma, Skye says.

Topsy winks.

She's been known to wink before.

But still…

Rabbits

Kim Goldberg

One morning the
landscape got up and
walked away. The rabbits
were the first to notice. No
grass to flirt in, no earth to
tunnel, no gardens to decimate.
Each rabbit gazed at its colleagues suspended
in empty space. There was still an abundance
of sky. But the horizon was as vague as a pointillist
painting, having no terrain to conjoin. No union of heaven
and earth, as the Daoists would say. With more free time
on their paws, the rabbits spent much of it copulating.
There was little else to occupy them. When the other
species took measure of their collective situation and the
impact of rampant rabbit fornication, the Animal
Kingdom passed anti-copulation laws (which were really anti-rabbit
laws because the other species knew how to keep their privates
private or read a book or resort to auto-erotic techniques if need
be). The rabbits soon had enough progeny of voting age to repeal
the anti-copulation laws and enact new laws mandating the
construction of sexual amusement parks in every town. There
were no raw materials with which to build these amusement parks
or towns. So these items remained mental constructs until enough
creatures had passed away from starvation that their bones could
be used for scaffolding and their hides for tent canvas, awnings,

slides, water beds, camel cabanas and many other applications. Rabbit hedonism ensued for quite some while, with the other species sulking in the bleachers. Until one day, under a blue sky adrift in tufted clouds, a new landscape arrived seemingly out of nowhere. Much coitus interruptus occurred. The other species cheered and scurried to anchor themselves to the earth.

This caused the new landscape (which was really an old and arthritic landscape that had been on the road too long) to drop dead from a heart attack.

No one noticed.

This story is also available as an audio version read by the author.
See page 241 for more details, or visit dark-mountain.net/issue-18-fabula-audio

Illustrations by **Bethan McFadden**

Mehel

Micheál Mac Gearailt

Meitheal: neighbours coming together to save the crops,
gather the turf; the process of mutual aid.

'Mrs. Leahy went quare last week.'

'Oh. Where?'

'She leapt the sod past the petrol station. Or maybe the bank. One
of the wild spots up there. Dju remember, Keera love?' She glances in
the rear-view mirror; her eyes meet mine as I tear them from the
window.

'Hm. Who?'

'Mrs. Leahy. She works in the tyre factory. Can't drive. Dju remember where she leapt the sod?'

I feel my father tense in the passenger seat. I've been home too
long.

'No. I forgot.'

I hadn't.

We are a misplaced people. We never belonged on this tiny island;
thus our process of constant disarticulation. We boil our flesh, gnaw
our bones, and send them flying to the four corners of the earth. We
belong on choppy seas, eternal maelstroms, vast laughing plains and
unbound skies; in lieu, we cling to the underbellies of metropolises
and offices, railroads and democracy. We belong anywhere but here.

This is what I tell myself as we drive into the bog. The dust surges
before us as we speed down the cratered causeway road, rising and
falling in perfect hymn. It is three months home; three months since

the evacuation, and him. I don't talk to the folks about it. It is high summer, with my days in the bog, nights staring into the screens of pocket gods getting ghosted. Three long years.

We pull up to the parking lot, fumbling out, and line up under the blaring sun. An overseer materialises in that quiet way they do, with the easy stride and cheek-splitting smile that I have yet to get used to. They told me I would. The folks have; they smile back.

'Welcome! ID please?'

'231,' my mother croaks.

'Fantastic! Your proofing?'

We lift our sleeves, in unison; we are one. The tattoos shimmer in the heat, unsure of their solidity.

The overseer blinks, blinks again, and smiles further. Perfect teeth. Sharpened.

'Welcome Mary, Jim, Keera; you're all good. Day 12 – we're almost done. Head on down, and have another great day at mehel!'

Glance at the sign. M-E-H-E-L. We once spelled it differently, this word which unites us. We have no need for outdated orthographies, old diesel engines unheard in their excess of i's, t's and h's.

We slunk past the truck, skidding down the causeway embankment to the edge of our plot. A gust of wind hits, drags my eyes skywards, filling my nose with rancid oil. The bog uncurls around me, a puckered rim of a plain pissing its way outwards for miles and miles to every horizon, sprawling confidently in her own perpetuity. At the edges, the barbed fences sway to unheard music in the searing sun. No unauthorised entry. I am authorised.

Our plot is half a hectare of thirty-three rows of lazy brown turf, stretching five thousand metres – no further and no less – which stop, distinctly, sixteen metres from the barrier. The Carmodys' above us. The Redmonds' below. Though we cannot see Carmodys' turf – we keep our eyes to ourselves – we heard whispers that it was blacker than ours, and would surely see them through another ice age, never mind a winter – so we cut their phone lines in the night. Big Redmond and his man could be heard like bulls rutting through the house. We laughed the night away.

'Keera love?'

'Yeah mam?'

'Will you gwan down to the bottom few rows by the ditch and see if they're ready for turning?'

I mutter agreement.

We stand for a moment uncertain, homoousios. It is difficult to forget the slow, squelching unravelling of mind and tongue that happens in this place. You feel it the moment you pass the gates. A slow buzzing in the throat, some wasp laying little, uncertain eggs. The bog is too wide, too open; only on the far-flung edges can we see the low patchwork hills with perfect places to hide. This place is the silence after the orgasm, the burning sensation of almost-memory leaving you sad and unsatisfied. We are unsuited to open space; it leaves no room for shame.

I turn and walk. Causeway to my right, comforting in its edge and definition, with the bog to my left. Its softness makes me nervous. I trail the dusty rut with precision, filling the form of every footprint left before me, an arrow sludging slowly north. I am careful not to step on the heather; it is unsanctioned and indecent, and furthermore dangerous; the wind and sun and weedkiller has left it vengeful. It is bleached, like the hair of a girl named Ashling.

I am at the end of our plot – row 33. The sods are unturned, and the grass has giggled its way through the grikes to stand, perversely, a slow sigh on the wind.

The sods sit; row on row of little brown bricks, churled out by royal procession. The machine gathers the raw contents in her apron, strolls slowly through the bog; excretes. The unformed turf passes through the hole and emerges, compressed, a perfect sod ready for life. Rows and rows shooting northwards, cockroach eggs or snail-trail. Each sod must be turned, again and again, meticulously; each side must face the sun.

Seeing the sods laid out, I am reminded of the Holocaust. They laid the bodies out like this, and made the Germans come and ogle at their crime. It is strange driving in here, every day, into the colony. As the diggers and tractors cleave deeper into the peat, cracking beers and celebratory paeans, I can feel, just for a moment, the pride of Leopold in his Congo. It is intoxicating.

The sods were once known to talk, if turned too soon. We were instructed not to listen. Each year we take our harvest, unearthing vast trees and fishheads, idols of dead gods and riverbeds; those are thrown away. Our chattel are self-replenishing, now miraculously dumb and mute.

Neither the anxious before nor the remorse of the after. In the action, consequence flees past you, licking your nose and then melting away. Treacherous whore. In the in-between we are caught up in the nowness, the skyhigh will to power. I wonder how the Russians felt on the eve of the Revolution, the Chinese in the aftermath of Tiananmen. We know only the ecstasy of war.

Unthinkable thoughts. Gone too long.

I bend down – I can still bend.

I don't wear gloves. The cold slush of turf is thrill to the skin. Beating drums and warhorses.

I pick up each one solicitously. Testing. Small brown edges. Fits in the palm; just. It has been a hot summer, the hottest we have known, and the turf's skin is tanned and stiff. I break it open; resist the urge to bite.

Ah yes. Wet and unmitigated. I feel saliva rise in my throat, dancing circles on my tongue. There is cooking to be done. It is too wet to be taken in – too malleable for history, we might draw blood. Let's wait for it to dry and desiccate.

I turn the first sod, content; the grass beneath will die. Then another; then another. Five thousand metres of slow, succulent rotation, one long spit without a pig.

Sometimes I wish we could disappear. Like Mrs. Leahy, like Shaun

Michaels and the Kearneys. That last one was a shock; a whole family going quare. The priest talked about it in Mass. Sometimes I go and look at their son's Facebook; we've all gone to the page of a dead man.

If we were to leap the sod, immaculate and unsullied; in trying to identify us, they would find our PPSNs wet and squelching, our bank accounts covered in some cold unintelligible filth.

One-third of the row done, I found a bog body.

'Mam – dad – another one.' My voice is carried by the eager wind, and my mother and father stand, blinking stupidly. Approach.

We prise the leathery skin out of the ground. Its neck is twisted wonderfully, encased by braided rope. Looped earrings hang from its lobes, and two frog eyes croak softly in the sun. It is naked; my mother blushes. Its ballsack swings, lugubrious. We are holding it aloft now, six hands on one corpse. I stare at my father who stares at my mother who stares at the balls. Dad watches telly in the sitting room, while Mam watches in the kitchen; the same programme, but the kitchen telly has the slightest delay, so that you can always hear one echo repeating the other. Mam always knows what will happen. They leave the door open, and sometimes discuss the episode if I am not locked in the bathroom.

We hoist the body higher, feeling our throats tickling with hints of asphyxiation. Their fears live on after death. Carry it over the hoppers, southwards, to the ditch. As we approach it we feel our unease rising, hackles on end, the slow, disjointed crescendo rising to climax. Ringing in the ears. The demarcation line. We reach it, filled with bubbling, black, sluggish water. The ground beyond is wild and unkempt, with thorny spines of heather boasting too-bright bells with phallic pride. I break a sweat at the sight.

Phone-signal weakens as you approach the separation line; they're fixing that – installing towers.

We chuck the body; it flies over the ditch, landing softly on the other side with a soft yawp. We scramble back, deeper into our plot. The unease subsides.

'How long have we been here?' my mother asks, breaking the silence.

My father is annoyed. 'An hour.'

'And how much left?'

'One more.'

'It feels longer. I'm dying to get back to the telly.'

'Yera.'

He turns to me.

'Call them there to take it away. They haven't eaten in a few months.'

With that they slink away, back to turn their own rows.

I turn back to the ditch, opening my windpipe with slow, deliberate relish. My tongue meets my teeth and laughs.

'Heeeeeeere suc suc suc suc! Heeeeeere suc suc suc suc suuuc!'

My call echoes across the bog. Far in front of me I see the ramshackle tents stir; cloth and calfskin sheets, plastic and galvanise heaped together in rickety sheds and shelter. A village or favela, camp or booley; this festering amalgamation eludes definition. A lone alder tree, sickly and leafless, hangs heavy over the twenty or so crumbling structures.

They reach the boundary in minutes, racing and whooping over the wild heather. My eyes watch, red-rimmed and watering; I tear away, returning to the sods.

Rotate. Step. Rotate. Step. Keeping my eyes on the ground, I hear them stampeding to the body, howling and popping round its leathery neck. I feel safe. The ditch is between us, impassable. I hear them drag the body back into the wild heather, back to their slum. I glance quickly, rapidly; I see leaves growing from ears, tiger tattoos, mottled ten-toed feet and eyes blinking lazily in chests. Dozens of them.

One form remains in the corner of my eye. I glance east; my folks are busy turning. I unbend my back, looking over the ditch. My breath catches in my throat.

'Mrs. Leahy?'

Her sweet smile is long gone; replaced by a cold, hard prune. Her skin is dark and windworn, and hair has begun to sprout all over her arms.

'Am Sweeney now.' Her voice is lighter, easier, sharper. She laughs, and the wind laughs with her. 'Biolar?'

'What?'

She blinks. 'Watercress.' Smiles.

I stand dumbly, working my mouth in slow circles. Head down. Keep turning.

'Am virulent.' She says. 'Am Baptist, headless cock-bashing vestibule grinding knuckles, announcing the arrival. Even pissing has become a sacred act.'

I try my best to ignore her. She continues.

'The empty place in guts is filled with roving fingers oozing mana and honey – am androgyny, hermaphroditus, Teresa after the ecstasy filled with cum of the godhead. Am poisonous sex, phallic teeth spitting out vulvic flecks pruning chaos in the formless sky above. Am the fishy aftermath of the schmundie. Am –'

I grasp a sod; firmly. Fire it at her face.

It misses. Our eyes meet. Hers are green. She pauses.

'Will ye come chousin' with us on the high gurt?'

With that she whirls and runs away.

I keep turning.

The sun rolls over my back. I love him for his virility, and detest him for darkening my skin. I envy him.

I look up. Mrs. Leahy has reached the camp; they are dancing round the bog body singing songs of praise. Firesmoke rises to the sky.

The ditch smoulders. Moss and scum gurgle in the boghole.

My phone vibrates in my pocket; far away, I hear a curlew. Or maybe a cuckoo. I forget.

I stand at the edge of the ditch. My ears scream.

I leap the sod. I fly.

This story is also available as an audio version read by the author.
See page 241 for more details, or visit dark-mountain.net/issue-18-fabula-audio

Enviro

Mike Cipra

When the virus went contagious, I was working as a park ranger at Mesa Verde National Park, where ancient humans once built safe-houses in the cliffs and ground corn with stones and cooked squirrels over smoldering juniper fires. A thousand years later, it appeared to be a stroke of luck to be up in those cliffs when the world finally evolved something that could out-digest *Homo sapiens*. My colleagues in other, less remote national parks had very different experiences.

Edgar Allan Poe House, the National Historic Site in downtown Philadelphia, was sacked. Poe's original manuscripts were recycled in the streets. I watched a live feed on my phone – for the entire minute and a half of shaky footage, the swollen mob chanted in chorus, 'Nev-er-more, Nev-er-more,' while stories and poems written by Poe's own hand were pulped and recycled in the streets. By sundown, the infected had transformed Poe's former residence into a free-range raven rookery, and people were hand-feeding chunks of sandwich to big black birds from the windows of Poe's historic house.

In Washington, DC, citizens presumably infected with the virus moved on the National Mall with hoes and shovels in hand. This viral mob chose an agricultural path of change, tearing out the Kentucky bluegrass growing between the Lincoln and Washington Monuments and atop the Vietnam Memorial, with its names of the dead inscribed in black stone. In place of turf, people tilled the soil and planted organic green beans, tomatoes, potatoes, broccoli, onions, and rainbow chard.

Within days, the virus had spread up coastlines and into every nation's heartland, coursing along interstates as if those great asphalt marvels of our dying civilisation were a collective bloodstream, leap-frogging oceans on the flight and shipping lanes, disregarding borders and walls and cultural differences like the great plagues do.

News report, breaking: 'The CEO of Humboldt Redwood Company has announced today that he will be transferring all of the company's coastal redwood forest lands to the Indigenous people who lived among the world's tallest trees for centuries before the sawmills arrived.' Streaming on Facebook live: the Yurok and Wiyot tribal councils accept title deeds and promptly burn them in a small fire, the papers smoldering beneath the towering redwoods. Smoke and steam rise in the wet Humboldt County morning. 'Today the world is renewed,' a Yurok woman in the frame says. 'I learned from my grandmother, and she from her grandmother, we do not cut these trees down. We wait for their lives to end naturally, for these ancients to blow over in a storm after collecting a thousand years of sun and rain. And only then will we build our canoes from their bodies, here, with gratitude on the forest floor.' She points to the massive *Sequoia sempervirens* rising to the sky behind her. 'If you cut this tree down, how the hell can you expect the boat made from its body to carry you and your family safely when you are crossing troubled waters?'

That first-person account, the way she explained her cultural relationship with a tree, the small fire of glowing legal documents turning to ash, it all touched off something electric in me. There's something you should know, before we go any further. Years ago, I camped in one of those giant coastal redwoods in Headwaters Forest. More accurately: I lived in a three-hundred-foot-tall tree that began growing from seed before Jesus Christ was born, in order to keep a living thing from being cut down and turned into shingles and money.

At Mesa Verde, we monitored the outside world continuously in those first hours of the pandemic. The flow of information was instant and everywhere and when reality began folding on itself, it was like a drug to have access to all of the windows and doors simultaneously, commanding your consciousness while the shared assumptions of our civilisation melted away and human societies transformed into a series of previously unthinkable scenes.

In Palm Springs, tan retirees joyfully diverted water from golf courses they had been driving carts and golf balls across only hours earlier, in order to restore the region's native California fan palm oases.

Sharks, sea otters, stingrays, sea horses, jellyfish, even starfish and sponges were liberated from the world's great aquariums and returned to the ocean. Schoolchildren carefully lifted organisms from touch-tanks and carried them to the sea for release.

The obliteration of Mount Rushmore was the first sign that the virus was not just about organic vegetables and happy harbour seals, that it was also activating a hot allele of violence in our genes. In super-slow-motion replay on YouTube, I watched a wave of nitro-glycerine swell at thirty times the speed of sound as it erased the iconic white male faces of America. Fire and stone shuddered along that wall of ancient granite in South Dakota, and I thought, *Welcome back to Earth, gentlemen.* I pressed play, to watch it again.

Two hours later, eco-terrorists targeted the Glen Canyon Dam. I call them eco-terrorists not because I am trying to brand them as enemy combatants, but because I know them as I know myself; I know their tactics and I understand their vision of the world as corrupt because I helped develop our vision. I know their dreams as my dreams because I have slept with them and woken up naked beside them and looked in the mirror wanting for it to be a stranger staring back, really wishing for it to be a stranger, still recognising the blue light of the believer behind my eyes.

Tons of dam concrete crumbled in an instant, unleashing a flood that killed more than five hundred people downstream. The leader of Earth Forever posted a video online, taking responsibility and calmly explaining the slow burn of transformation that was taking over our species.

I felt lightheaded as I watched the woman speak. She called herself Pachamama in the video – so pretentious – and she had a few more hard lines on her face, but there was no mistaking her for any other person on the planet. Silvia still possessed the same terrifying, beautiful purpose she carried like a secret in her body when I lived with her on the Lost Coast of California. There were rattlesnakes on that beach. We fought and fucked and gathered our own food in the midst of that wilderness, my ego breaking against hers every day like waves against the rocky coast. Or maybe she was the ocean, and I was the land being worn away. Two years later, she had convinced me to camp in the branches of an old-growth redwood with her. And if I am honest, we saved that grove of trees through the force of her will, not mine.

'It is time to apologise to Mother Earth,' my ex-wife said, smiling. 'I want to hear all of you say you're sorry. And this time, you're going to fucking mean it.'

Pachamama proceeded to outline the situation, as if she were speaking to children. Earth Forever had developed a world-changing virus in a remote laboratory over the last seven years, perfecting the infection they called the Green Goddess. (Like the salad dressing? Come on.) Then, a month ago, they had released their virus to incubate in the world's great cities. London, Lima, Los Angeles, Bangkok, Berlin, Bogota, Shanghai, Sao Paolo, Seoul – her list of viral epicentres continued with the logic of a lullaby, branching like a tree across the Earth's surface – Kinshasa and Cairo, Delhi and Dhaka, Tehran and Tokyo, Jerusalem and Jakarta.

'We targeted the highest population centres and spread our efforts across continents. Based on conservative mathematical modelling, we anticipate complete worldwide colonisation in approximately a year,' she said. 'My friends, we're not spreading the common cold here. We're transforming the human animal. It's unhelpful, even counter-productive, to see this as a sickness you must fight. A sickness makes you weaker. This virus is the final step in our evolution toward balance with the Earth. Until you embrace the change that is happening to you, you'll just hurt yourself. Instead, approach this as an opportunity to get in touch with your better nature.'

She paused, looked into the camera, smiled.

'There may be some of you who have permanently severed your connection to a better nature. All I can say to you is: good luck baking your cake.'

The video ended with a replay of the Glen Canyon Dam exploding, Edward Abbey's dream of release and monkeywrenching made real, a waterfall of concrete and fire, the great Colorado River finally set free.

*

'Man, your ex is one crazy bitch,' Ruby said.

'When I first met her, Silvia was just a passionate girl who loved nature.'

'How does it feel to see her now, turning human civilisation into cat food?'

'My mind feels like it's full of bees,' I said. 'It's hard to think.'

'Well, you better fucking snap out of it,' Ruby said. 'It's easy to kill, even easier to watch it all turn to manure. But we have the responsibility to do something.'

'What can we do?'

'First, isolate ourselves from all those motherfuckers. Keep them away from us. And then, grow our own food, build our own society, have some kids, and raise a generation of humans who haven't been turned into zombies by a virus.'

'That's why I love you,' I said to Ruby. 'You see a problem, you meet it head-on, and you have so much strength and determination. But baby, I don't know if this is the kind of problem we can solve.'

'Wow, when the world's turning to ashes, you can really turn it on.'

'Do you honestly think the virus is that bad?' I asked. 'You've been watching with me: the infected are tearing out golf courses and restoring habitat. The Yurok and the Wiyot have been given back hundreds of thousands of acres of coastal redwood forest to steward. People are planting organic gardens. What if this isn't the end of the world, but the start of another, better chapter for the world?'

There was a long silence, like sandstone eroding.

'They just blew up the Glen Canyon Dam,' she said. 'That means anyone downstream on the Colorado River will be dead in a few minutes. I have friends who conduct plant surveys down in the Grand Canyon. Anna and Jane were on the river this week.'

'Jesus, I'm sorry. I didn't think ...'

Ruby took a deep breath. She had tears in her eyes.

'Ashkii, what happens when all of those poor infected bastards run out of dolphins to free? Do you think they might turn on themselves? Look, it's already happening. Just imagine seven billion feverish humans trying to save the Earth all at once, with no clue how to do it.'

'Maybe the point is that we're all supposed to try.'

'Jesus, you *want* to get infected, don't you!'

'Well, I accept the fact that it's probably going to happen.'

'I can't accept that,' she said. 'No one has the right to stick a hot virus in my body and watch me turn into a sack of fucking flaxseeds. Especially not your ex-wife. My God, this is a nightmare.'

Ruby stalked to the door and pulled on her river sandals.

'You going out?' I said.

'Yeah,' she said. 'I have to do *something* about this, Ash. Even if you can't be bothered.'

'Mind you don't catch a cold out there. Heard there's a bad one going around.'

She looked at me, stony-faced.

'You're an asshole,' she said finally. 'And no virus in the world is going to change that.'

The next day was Sunday, and we had just finished evacuating the park of all visitors. The park's superintendent, Cliff Kaiser, had ordered an emergency shutdown of the Mesa. No one in or out, until further notice. I knew it was Ruby's doing, by the way she was celebrating. She had mixed two Old Fashioneds with the last of our bourbon. Heavy on the bitters, with a bright maraschino cherry lodged in the ice like a flag planted on Antarctica.

We turned on the live feed, hungry for news from the outside world. Just about every website and video channel was broadcasting the same spectacle, live from the Superdome in New Orleans. We quickly found a site with decent production values: steady cameras, good sound quality, and multiple angles including close-ups.

Executives from Peabody Coal, from Anglo American, from Rio Tinto, from Exxon Mobil, from Shell Oil, from Weyerhauser and Monsanto and Barrick Gold and Blackwater and PNC Financing jogged in their designer suits through the players' tunnel. It was an all-star lineup of the world's worst environmental offenders. As they ran onto the field, a capacity crowd of seventy-three thousand greeted the executives with a torrent of boos. There was a tremendous appetite in the crowd's cresting roar of disapproval. The camera crew went in for close-ups of the men's faces. Their expressions showed the resolve that had shaped their careers. These guys were in it to win it.

An obese oil executive was the first to step forward, carrying a lifetime of steak and butter on his frame. You could have stored a Fabergé egg in the waddle hanging from his chin. The public address announcer read off a list of the man's career accomplishments. As a young oil industry lobbyist, he had paid elected leaders to deliver billion-dollar corporate tax breaks for oil companies. As the Environmental Protection Specialist for Shell Oil, he was responsible for the cover-up of a catastrophic oil spill in the Niger Delta. And when promoted to Vice President, he pioneered the oil industry practice of suppressing climate change science.

With each new revelation, there was a fresh wave of booing from the crowd. When the list of crimes had been fully exposed, the offences laid bare, a handsome young man jogged out to the executive, holding a red plastic gas can. The executive took the can and, without a moment's hesitation, doused himself. He choked on liquid gasoline and coughed through the acrid fumes. He fell to his knees and vomited. As he vomited, the crowd cheered wildly. The handsome young man whipped a white towel over his head, urging the crowd to make more noise. Then, he took the empty gas can and skipped back to the sidelines.

There was a slow pan across the stadium's spectators. Some were dressed in homemade costumes: trees and turtles, kangaroos and koalas. Others were partially or even completely naked, many bodies smeared with bright paint, strangers with arms wrapped around one another's shoulders in solidarity. One topless woman was bearing aloft a hand-painted sign that read, *The Earth is a Tough Mother*. The camera held on her for several seconds before fading into a shot of the oil executive in the centre of the field, dripping with the refined product he had devoted his life to removing from the ground and encouraging us all to burn, profligately. The fat man stood, breathing hard. He removed a gold Zippo lighter from his pocket and held it in the air. The crowd roared. The executive smiled with something that looked like relief. This was his moment of absolution, his most perfect confession. He gestured for the fans to make more noise. The crowd started singing Queen's timeless anthem: 'We will, we will, rock you! Rock you!' The executive turned around three hundred and sixty degrees, saluting the entire stadium. Then, he flicked the lighter open with his thumb and sparked it.

On TV, you could hear the crowd scream like a tornado through his open mouth as he burned. He was alive with the pain. Television cameras tried to focus on the man's eyes, but waves of heat distorted the image, blurring his humanity, melting away all sense from his sacrifice.

The screen winked off.

'Ruby, could you please turn the feed back on?'

'I don't want to watch anymore,' she said, her eyes brimming with tears.

'I really need to understand what's happening out there.'

'Should I make you some nachos, so you can watch the world end with a full stomach?'

'Look, if we can bear to watch the things that are happening in the infected world, we'll better understand the extent of the disease.'

'You know the extent of the disease,' she said. 'You were married to the creator of the fucking disease!'

'This isn't about my ex-wife.'

'Sure it is. She and her pals are the ones bringing about the historic destruction of the human race. Do you get how fucked up this is? Do you like watching this?'

Somewhere inside, near the core, I knew that I did like watching the virus transform our dying civilisation, and this feeling frightened me.

'Look, I just want to know what's happening to the world. And to do that, I need to witness the horror. Looking away from it isn't going to help.'

'You're scaring me,' she said. 'I mean it, Ashkii, there's part of you that is fundamentally warped. I thought that the warp in you was kind of cool when we first met. You know, a mark of character, like when an old tree gets a twist in its trunk from growing on the side of a mountain. But now, I think it's a flaw.'

She threw the remote on the coffee table and walked out of the house. I thought about following her. Instead, I picked up the remote and turned the screen back on.

The camera focussed on one man in a well-tailored suit, standing behind a dump truck. The dump truck was filled with fine black soot. The bed of this truck lifted slowly, on an increasingly steep angle, its tailgate holding back an avalanche. The public address announcer said that the man standing in the shadow of the truck had brokered deals to fund mountaintop removal coal mining. On the screen, a text crawl listed the mining operations he had enabled in Appalachia.

Cut to the crowd. There was a young boy, his face smudged in black, holding one end of a banner that read, *Coal: It will take your breath away.*

The image returned to the coal financier. Unlike the oilman, this guy did not appear to be enjoying the opportunity for atonement. He was sweating and shaking. The coal financier gestured to the sidelines and held his hands in the posture of prayer. The bed of the truck stopped moving, and the crowd booed. The handsome young man jogged out again, this time holding a microphone.

'Is there something you'd like to say?' asked the young man.

The stadium quieted. The coal financier's image appeared on the stadium's Jumbotron.

'I'm not sure I want to go through with this anymore,' he said.

Boos rained down. As the young man tried to pull away the microphone, the coal financier held onto it desperately.

'Listen, I can change. I have changed, since I caught this virus. The virus is the best thing that's ever happened to me. As it is for all human beings, and for the Earth. I know the things I've done were awful. Just awful.'

He tried to swallow sobs as the raw hatred of the crowd and the magnitude of the moment overtook him. Tears and coal dust streaked his face.

'Please forgive me,' he beseeched. 'I know I've been awful. I know that. But I want to work for a healthy planet now. I want to make amends with Mother Earth. I have skills that I will dedicate entirely to the future of our planet.'

The young man succeeded in yanking the microphone away with a whipping tug that produced a short, sharp screech of feedback. He turned to the crowd.

'What do you think, brothers and sisters? After all he has done, does this criminal deserve a second chance?'

The crowd booed loudly.

The young man went on, feeding on the crowd's energy: 'Ask yourself this: Do those mountains he removed get another chance?'

On the Jumbotron, the image of a pulverised crater flickered, and then held.

'How about the fish he killed with industrial runoff?'

On my screen, the crowd at the Superdome was replaced by stark images of trout that had gone belly-up and had washed up on the banks of a blackened river. Their mouths were open. Their eyes were white and clouded over.

The broadcast cut back to the Superdome, as the crowd began chanting: 'Coal kills, coal kills, coal kills!' The young man smiled. He turned to the financier.

'Looks like you've dug your own grave. Now have a little dignity, and let us enjoy our fucking justice.'

The young man jogged away. The financier stood still, understanding and finally accepting his role in the great pageant. The tailgate of the truck swung open with a bang. Soot smothered him within seconds. They showed two different angles on slow-motion replay, and I could watch the impact of the soot knocking him down before covering his body and suffocating him. On the bottom of the screen, the chyron read: 'Next: congressman who denied climate science throughout career will tighten razor wire around his own neck, tie wire noose to scaffold, and stand on block of melting ice…'

I turned off the feed and walked outside, into the late spring sunshine. Wild turkeys were walking through the yard. Ruby was watching them intently.

'They've moved from suicide to murder,' I said.

'So it's time for popcorn, then?'

'Maybe it's not the best thing, this virus. Maybe its effect on us is more complex.'

'Really? That's as far as you're willing to go? Look, while you're busy running the moral calculus on murder, we need to cut Mesa Verde off from the rest of the world," she said. 'We need to isolate ourselves before this virus arrives.'

'I thought that was the point of the visitor evacuation you and Cliff Kaiser pulled off today.'

'It wasn't enough. We need to physically and permanently cut ourselves off – now, before it's too late. Blow up the road. Seal out the virus. Separate from the infected.'

'Blowing up the road will sever our link to food.'

'We'll grow our own food. Corn, beans, and squash, just like the ancestors of the Pueblo people did. I've been growing my demonstration fields up here for the last three years, using the old seed stock, imitating their techniques. You've seen my gardens. You know I can do it.'

'There's a difference between a handful of demonstration gardens for tourists and providing enough food for the survival of a society. Even a small society like ours would be.'

Ruby nodded at the wild turkeys as they pecked and gobbled in our front yard.

'We'll eat turkey and deer and whatever's left in our pantries while we clear and plant additional fields. We have enough seeds, trust me. The superintendent says our million-gallon water tank is full.'

'You've talked with Cliff about this.'

'Of course. He's very much like you. Wringing his hands about how to fill his belly, unconcerned as a daisy about catching a virus that will turn his brain into kombucha.'

'Even a million-gallon water tank will eventually run dry.'

'Of course. When it runs dry, we'll turn to the natural springs in the cliffs. We'll collect our water as the ancient people did.'

'What if we're already infected?' I asked.

'What do you mean?'

'The choices we're making, right now, this moment – what if our brains are already being influenced by this virus?'

She laughed.

'I'm not crazy.'

'Crazy people never think they're crazy. That's one of the symptoms. You just proposed blowing up the only road in or out of Mesa Verde and feeding ourselves through subsistence farming. Objectively, those are some end-of-the-world choices.'

'No, they're practical choices to avoid catching this fucking virus.'

'Look, I'm just proposing that we ask whether we are in our right minds before we destroy our escape route and our main artery to food. I'm not calling you crazy, Ruby. I'm asking us to make a determination, together, about whether or not we're already infected.'

There was a long silence, like sunlight on stone.

'OK,' she said finally. 'Without a lab or a doctor or any knowledge of how this sickness works, how do you propose to determine whether we're infected?'

'We could observe how the virus makes people act,' I said. 'And then we could test to see if we're acting that way.'

'OK, how exactly is the virus making people act? Come on, Ashkii. You know her, you know how she thinks. What would *she* want a virus like this to do?'

I took a deep breath. The memory of wind-whipped sand against our bare skin. Rattlesnakes on the beach.

'Silvia always wanted us to care more about other life than our own.'

'I think you nailed it,' Ruby said.

There was another silence, this one like the water under a frozen lake.

Finally, Ruby said, 'I have a test to propose.'

'Tell me.'

'We need to kill something beautiful – something natural and perfect – to prove we're not infected.'

'A turkey,' I said quickly, looking at the flock now moving through the neighbour's yard. 'We'll kill a turkey and roast it.'

'No, a turkey's too useful. For this test, we need to commit a completely pointless murder of another living thing in order to prove our mental health. Now think. What out here do you feel is incredibly, impossibly beautiful?'

'You are,' I said.

'*That's* funny, you fucking psycho,' she said. 'Come on, take a look around you. This shouldn't be hard.'

I could see then what she was asking me to do. It was as clear to me as the rings in the heart of a juniper. She closed the distance between us, until her mouth was up against my ear.

'You lived in a tree,' she whispered. 'You lived in an old-growth redwood to prevent it from being chopped down and turned into wood beams and dumb profit. How long were you up there, Ash?'

'Two hundred seventy-three days,' I said numbly.

'It's such an amazing thing you did,' said Ruby. 'That's why I love you. Because you're capable of so much compassion and generosity for other living creatures. You know that, right?'

'That tree gave me more than I ever gave it. I ate meals and had sex and read books up there. It was my home.'

'We'll need to cut down an old-growth tree, Ash. You and the ex had a redwood together. You and me, we get to take down a juniper that has survived wind and sun and frost and drought for six hundred years.'

'You're asking me to do something that will hurt me.'

'This test was your idea. Listen, I'll help you. We'll do it together. Lover, we're going to kill a tree for absolutely no reason, other than to show we can. That's how we prove our sanity.'

This is an excerpt from a novel in progress, Enviro

[167]

Stricken

Luna Mrozik Gawler

Illustrations by **Petra Carlson**

The camel and I are the only ones left. When the wind quiets, it's the stillness that's impossible to take. Unbearable after too many days and decades of rhythm and responsibility. And now what? Now the pens are empty, and nothing carves or shifts the stubborn horizon. There are no horses to tend. You took the dog when you left. I wander about as though there is still a job to be done. Map the stripped bodies of mulga trees where they lie low, bullied into a height the cattle could reach in their desperation. I kick the dust and scratch my own sums into the dirt, counting the days until the water runs out.

Your request has been logged with the Ministry of Growth and Agriculture.
Your case number is 041031

We met in a drought. My Dad suffering in his illness, bringing as many hands from town as he could to keep the farm going. Keep the water filling the troughs in the morning. More than I could do alone while Nan took care of the house and Dad's needs. Those days were the first of the real heat. The first time we couldn't work past sunrise. I was already beaten by the time Dad agreed to hire help. And you came, the lot of you, one at a time, driving in from town, sturdy and clean. One summer and I'd have done anything for you with that smile, bright enough to feel like I could have found my way home in a sand-storm as long as you were outside smiling in my direction. That first date you came to the house to fetch me in your father's ute, the tyres spitting orange into the air above the road. Like it was a proclamation, like you were a prophecy being fulfilled, swept in on the searing earth itself. You ruptured the flat blue of the afternoon with a bouquet made from the long-fingered leaves of the mulga tree. So proud of yourself for the ingenuity and my surprise when you thrust the knotty branches in my arms. Unstoppable, you said. Resilient. And we knew we would be. It wasn't long before we decided just to stay. You were always such a sucker for my Nan, and she'd seemed so shaken that one time we'd talked about leaving. And things were getting harder, and then they offered us the farm, if we'd marry.

I start furthest from the house and work my way back in. Not far by our old standards, only to the first line of fence, what now is just a suggestive snake of rust and toppled timber in the thirsty dirt. I start early, and loop my way around the edges, circling in as the sky peels and rids itself first of the heavy indigo of night, and then the soft marmalade of dawn, interrupted only by the dark dot of an eagle, easing its way across the expanse, mimicking my arc. Or preceding it, one of us the instigator and the other playing ghost. By the time the hard blue of day has set in, and the heat starts to build eagerly in the red dirt, my footprints are fresh by the mailbox and I am back inside, safe before the sun has had a chance to spot me.

The house is dark in the day now. I stay still, flat backed on the floor. The Laminex has taken the heat badly, cracked and curled towards the ceiling fan like an insult, a vulgar gesture of decay, a vague threat, or an omen breathed in from the baking air and made visible. I pass the day watching the flies sweeping in and out of the kitchen, dutifully orbiting the dust on the table, in case it has trans-formed into food since the last expedition.

With the encouragement of the heat, the dirt began practices of migration. Dunes appeared where flat plains had been. Trees were devoured, and sometimes only the highest tips of dead branches could be seen arching towards the cloudless sky.

We lost the back shed in one bad night, the desert sliding in while we slept, spitting red dust under the back door and slipping its way towards the bedroom. Opening the door onto the morning I heard you swear over the sound of brushing my teeth and nearly fell for the way I ran to see. The shed buried, the old door caved in. One of your dogs had been sleeping in there. It took four of the boys a week to get the dirt out, get your tools back, bury the body on purpose this time.

The cartography had changed. Chunks of stone and the arc of cattle ribcages, jawbones, teeth suddenly littered the space around the house and fences, as though they had erupted in some undetected quake. It was soothing, to slip out into the night and gather them, leaving you bent over the calculator with the burden you refused to share. In a sky so endless, the stars are impeccable. A fortress of hope, dazzling in the deep infinity of an outback sky. With the torch turned off, it was as though the starlight was caught in each flint of rock, each jag of porcelain bone that stuck up and grinned toothily towards the sky. With one eye closed, the soil became a field of stars, and the sky a field of bone, and I could tip off the edge of the Earth, falling into the slow spin of a luminous sky.

Thank you for your enquiry. Your enquiry is important to us.
The Ministry of Growth and Agriculture is experiencing a higher level of demand than usual. Our first available officer will respond to your query as soon as possible. We thank you for your patience.

When we started cutting the mulgas, I was reluctant, but you promised it wouldn't last. That the rain was a week away, three at the most. At the end of that first day, you boys sat in your sagging camp chairs laughing under your ragged hats and dusty shirts as Darcy did a rain dance. The headlights catching the ornament of tinnies and making their greens and reds incandescent, frivolous against the weight of what had just begun. Raindance, you said later, and shook your head, laughing. But I saw you, the next night, and the night after, walking out behind the shed, and from the kitchen window I could see your shadow begging the clouds to bring their counsel back to the thirsty places, to keep the last of the dams from drying.

I don't look for you. I don't go far enough. I don't want to see you as the sun changes your skin to hide, the way it has turned the cattle to leather, skin parched and cracked, stretched and torn over the ribs and rotted tongues.

I wait for the grief, think of my Nan, stoic to the end. Not a tear when Dad went. Or Dad when he first found the note from Mum, skipped out. Him standing so still at the kitchen bench and then just putting on his hat, pushing out the back door, climbing the tractor and heading to the top paddock. Maybe that's where you went. Or are. Two thousand bullets is an impossible number. Two thousand and one if you count the last dog. Two thousand and two altogether.

You got stronger in those last weeks. Mornings spent dragging the weight of limp kangaroos from the water troughs every morning, climbed in to drink and too weak to climb out. You told me you had stopped counting the bodies piled up in the last of the shade. But it was all counting then, the bigger numbers for volumes, bores, dams, feed. The little ones for bodies, neighbours retreating to the safety of the city, one pair at a time, and bullets.

One cow here or there. A roo, a horse. A slow accumulation like the flies building up on the window sill. How many dams were empty, how many tanks were low. Even the mulgas had gone bare, the sun burdening the thin branches with more heat than they could suffer. Thousands of dollars on cotton seed, chickpea, hay, five thousand acres of mulga, two thousand cattle. Gone.

The neighbours left in pairs, the trucks leaving orange smokestacks in the distance to announce the plain was a little less occupied. We'll stay, I said. We'll make it work. Whatever it takes. Resilience. When we were held in the soft touch of our bed I'd whisper 'The water truck is only a week away. Three at most.'

That night I dreamt a river spilled from the sink, the water pushing our bodies into new shapes, slipping our skin into scales, silver and quick. We breathed the wet deep through our gills, drew the water into our bodies and washed downstream. You twisting your tail in the sun. Dazzling.

If you are waiting for transport or water please contact the Ministry for Growth and Agriculture and quote reference number #7786

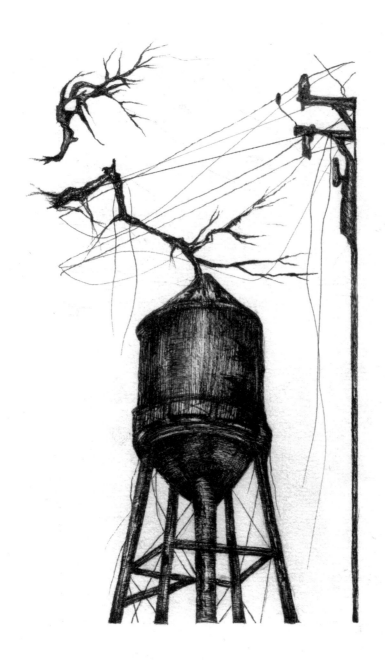

I walk out in the dark past the near empty water tanks, over the lonely stones that were the garden bed you made as a birthday present. I pass the kennel and its dry water bowl, pass the shed and the barren pens. The camel is still here with me, and I fill her trough with what little there is to offer. Under the heavy shore of her lashes, her eyes are the wettest place I've seen in months.

I pass the broken dozer, the cracked radiator of the ute, the bodies of the horses. I step into the endless, beyond our most human marks, moving quickly in the half light. The dust wakes as I walk, makes itself kin, slips up in the pre-dawn clarity and under the tongue of my boots, comes to rest between my fingers, behind my ears, settles in my hair. I do not bother to carry the crowbar, and drag its weight behind me.

I do the only job there is left to do. Crack the life out of bodies caught in the aching space between here and death. No bullets left now. When the circle loops back to the veranda, I do not bother to wipe the blood from the crowbar, or the dust from my skin. There is still no sign of the promised water truck.

We were together when we found the last dam was dry. You'd grown silent that week and we walked without words across the last scrub, the sun colluding with gravity, the heat threatening to drive us down to the very core of the Earth if we didn't keep moving. You saw it first. And I hung back as you walked steady, into the centre, put a palm flat where the last of the water had been. As though there might be a way to draw it back through the power of your wilful hands.

As you raised your hand, you spotted a shell in the dry mud, a fresh water shell from an ancient ocean. You looked at me then, and just like that, I saw the impossibility of it all rise up in you – as though for a moment you became that raging, untameable sea, and then all of a sudden, withdrew. You were gone. You stayed one more week, but your tide never came back in.

The water tanks are empty. There is still no truck. The radio offers me nothing, though I sit in dust and suffocation of the house and wait patiently. The horizon is visible from the front veranda now the trees lie where they fell, bulldozed in those last months. The heat has sucked the marrow from their trunks, bleached their skeletons and made them brittle.

It has been more than a week since I've seen anything in the sky other than stars. I heard the last of the butcherbirds leave the same day the taps went dry, their seesaw siren carving close to the bedroom roof while I lay listening for the radio. The hottest part of the day seems to be getting longer.

My Nan holds back the wings of the rooster, pinches its shoulders to reveal its neck, slices it hard and quick, tossing the body far enough away so the blood does not stain her apron. Her voice wakes me in the solitude of our bed, and I move before the day begins. Before I can think, or hesitate.

The stars are brighter for the cold. Their hardlight catches on the gutter of the house, and on the blade I carry from the kitchen. I do not wear shoes, it feels irreverent. The cool of the dirt made white by the last of the moonlight chills the soft places where my toes meet my soles. It feels heavy, like an anchor reaching up for the pit of me. I try not to retch when I reach her pen. She is tired under her long lashes, she has had no water for days and does not bother to move as I stroke her head. I hold my lips to the thick fold of her ears and say the most true things I can. That I am sorry. That we are the last ones left, and I need her help to get as far as the road.

I drive the knife hard into the base of her neck. Through the fur, I feel the muscle give way. I do not step back. The blood comes hot and wet, pours thick to the ground, and I do not move to avoid it. Let my skin think it is finally raining. It pools across my feet and breaks the drought, mud running sweet and dark from where we stand and heading for the open expanse of the desert. She groans as she topples, but does not seize, and does not panic. The wave of her turns to a trickle and finally a drip. When her tongue falls from her mouth, I am jealous of how wet it looks. Her hide is thick, but not as hard as it could be, as the sun rises I find her stomach, and slice it fast. There are not even flies left to witness her corpse. I am reluctant to leave you, wherever you are but still take the bottles I have filled with what water she had left, and head towards the horizon, towards the road, leaving red footprints in the dust as I go.

A truck has been dispatched with sufficient water for your property's requirements. Your case number is #065991. The Ministry thanks you for your patience and reminds you that the Farmers are our Future.

The Bell

Mark Martin

My first date with Soren was a kind of private dare, a challenge I set myself. We'd exchanged numbers at the opening of a Lower East Side gallery. The crowd had held us two strangers stationary beside each other so long I had to say hello. I wouldn't have bothered normally. He wore a face like a wet weekend and, in the harsh gallery light, the holes and snags in his sweater had nowhere to hide. He said contemporary art was advertising by other means and had to reel that one back when he heard I worked in marketing. Loneliness had driven him to the gallery, he explained.

Not a promising start, is it? But more plausible New York men had turned out to be duds. I took a gamble and called him later that week.

My thoughts went something like this. I'd left London for New York looking for change. Things had happened at home – an upsetting development with an old friend, a failed marriage – events that left my head spinning. Life had been bobbing along quite merrily, but all of a sudden I could hear the roar of rapids ahead. I was getting older. The years were sweeping me onward, and on either side dwelt possibility, territories unexplored, places that would drift by if I let them. His crystal-blue eyes came to me as I was drifting off to sleep, and in the morning I thought, 'Do something out of character, Joan.'

We met at a vegan restaurant in Bushwick, a halfway house for reformed grad students. The whole place smelled of Marmite. Boosting that Friday feeling was Leonard Cohen, grizzling through the speakers. My yoga gear seemed like the best outfit for the occasion, and I arrived straight from class, a bit pink in the face. That didn't stop me feeling overdressed. But Soren put me at ease. When I came in, he was curled over a book. He wasn't posting updates about being kept waiting by his date. He didn't even look up when the door opened. Next, when I said his name, he was unexpectedly attentive, standing to extend a hand. He pulled out the table so I could take the banquette, and when he started standing up, I thought he'd never stop. He was taller than I remembered, and height is very handy in a man; I like my partners to be visible in a crowd.

In a more flattering light, his looks were aristocratic, face narrow and long nose aquiline, floppy flaxen hair receding ever so slightly in a way that made him look raffish and vulnerable.

The conversation stumbled at first. I tried to keep it light – dating escapades, the shows I was streaming. He was polite. But his ears pricked up when I mentioned my friend back in London, the one who'd disturbed me so much. She heard voices in her head. She'd rejected conventional treatment and visited an ashram or something. The whole experience had been very upsetting.

The idea of an inner voice stirred Soren. It doesn't have to take the form of actual words, he said, like a hallucination. Messages erupt from within at times, like an instinct. He talked about Plato, and this idea that we know everything before we're born and that birth is a kind of forgetting. He said children entered the world trailing clouds of glory. Kids instinctively see animals as beings with an inner life as rich as ours, Soren thought, and that truth was suppressed as society closed in on them. He was very sweet – the eternal student.

He got quite intense, fixing me with those lovely, clear eyes. With a little spit and polish, he would have been a knockout. That was obvious. Words tumbled out of him and, along with his theories about nature and the sublime and whatnot, I started to pick up the outlines of a life.

At a university in Vermont, one of his teachers had set up a climate change action group, an organization that grew fast and gave Soren his first real job. When his mum got cancer, he quit and returned upstate to his family home near the Finger Lakes. After her death, he worked at an elephant sanctuary in Tennessee, the memory of which made his eyes glisten. He had spent time with Buddhist monks in Japan. As he moved from place to place, he was all the time haunted by thoughts of the damage being done to the planet; it kept him up at night, filled him with remorse, tied up his guts and put him off food. He'd been arrested on protests several times, and the District of Columbia was pursuing criminal proceedings against him for incitement to riot. What the human race was doing to the planet broke his heart, he said.

I concurred, of course. The environment is something I take very seriously.

'People need to think about what it'll do to GDP,' I told him.

Among the Buddhists of the Yamagata Prefecture, he had picked up some peculiar dietary habits, which I learned a little about that evening, although not enough to understand what was in store. While I looked over the menu and its various means of bloating, he explained that he had brought his own meal, prepared beforehand, and was paying the staff as if they'd made it for him. He had done this before, although not on dates, he quickly added.

'Perhaps I should have the same thing,' I said. He smiled ruefully and waved his hand over a little bowl of pine needles and nuts. It took me a moment to register that this gesture was an invitation. His dinner was basically a condiment.

'You can't live on that?'

I'll never forget his smile – wry, sad, and a bit shy.

'You don't expect everyone to eat like a mouse to save the planet, do you?'

He said in ancient Greece there were philosophers who lived like vagrants, sleeping in barrels, dressing in rags, mocking the lifestyle of the rich. They wanted to show people how little they really needed, in a consider-the-lilies-of-the-field kind of vein. They were like personal trainers, except they drove people to build virtue instead of muscle, pushing ordinary men and women, by the force of example, not to become as exceptional as them but simply to go a little further in the same direction. The story didn't mean much to me at the time.

I was meeting someone far outside my normal circle, someone *other*. Soren was interesting, and I felt like a reporter, which made the date an odd sort of success. Of course, he was very serious. I was careful not to wind him up with anything indelicate or, well, funny. The only joke I tried came just as we were leaving.

'I read a story online that some scientist thinks plants feel pain,' I said. 'What are the people at this place going to eat if that turns out to be true?'

On the sidewalk, very matter of fact, he asked if we were going to sleep together that evening. There was nothing cocky in his manner; he was quite gentlemanly about it.

'Oh, yes, I should think so,' I said.

That's when he asked me to punch him in the face.

'Is that one of those American expressions?' I said. 'You know, like "Gag me with a spoon"?'

But no. He genuinely wanted me to lump him one. A bit of rudimentary sadism was much more the kind of thing I'd expected than a lecture on nature and the human spirit. That didn't make it appealing.

'I didn't realise you were into kink.'

He didn't either apparently. He'd never, so he said, made this request before. I declined, because it was too weird. That made him embarrassed, and when he described having a block emotionally that needed to be broken, I took pity on him and went along with the idea. Perhaps we were both after something new. I slipped off my repurposed wedding ring and caught him with a jab from my right. After countless make-believe fights on the screen, a real punch is probably always likely to be a disappointment. The sound is wet and muffled compared to the metallic cracks and wallops of the action movies. But my punch sent him staggering, which was quite impressive. He was a full head taller than me.

'Yoga and pilates,' I said, flexing a bicep, 'two classes each, every week.' Wary, I added, 'This punching thing is a one-way street, right? I'm not getting into a fight, okay?'

On hearing my concern, he became very solicitous for a man who'd just been punched in the face. He told me not to worry. A little pain cleared his head. That's why he asked me to hit him. It was a sudden urge, and then he told me he hadn't been with a woman for three years.

'Are you into boys?' I asked.

No, he had simply, so he said, lost the urge. He was too sad. But then something happened. He'd injured his rotator cuff doing farm work at an intentional community near the Finger Lakes. A woman doctor had examined him. Her touch on his shoulder, probing the muscle, awoke such a plaintive feeling he was close to tears. That's what drove him to the gallery.

Under the streetlights, a little bruise took shape on his cheekbone. Lost and confused despite his impressive intelligence, a ghost of childhood in his eyes, he looked quite lovely.

'Let's go back to my place and look at that shoulder,' I said.

In my apartment, his naked body made me gasp. Soren was so thin. His pelvic bones put me in mind of insect exoskeletons; you could count every rib. But he was still lovely, in the right light. He was cool to the touch, and it was good to feel flesh so hard and smooth compared to the well-upholstered gents I'd dated so far in America.

There was no more violence that first time. Although he asked me to dig my nails into his skin, which I did until the blood threatened my manicure.

He was gentle and attentive making love. Engrossed in my body one moment, he would raise his head the next and look around, breaking the surface to draw breath before throwing himself back beneath the bedsheet. We fucked three times that night. When he left in the morning, he held my hand in both of his and thanked me like I was a nurse or a nun helping him through a final illness. Back in the office that day, I was all sweetness and light. This sad man had put a spring in my step.

We saw each other at intervals of between three and five weeks, by and large. I was travelling a lot with work, and at the time I believed travel was the only thing coming between us. For my friends and colleagues, he was a shadowy figure. He didn't meet more than a couple of them, but because he gave me so much to talk about, he became a constant presence in my life. In the eyes of friends and colleagues, he cast me in a new light. Prior to that point, I'd come across as an über-careerist, a sleek professional, a category that doesn't win many friends. And once people see you in a new light, you have the power to change.

We never ate out again. We would meet late in the evening or during the day and take walks together or watch old movies. He asked me to hurt him in some way almost every night we spent together. Once, things started to get steamy in the kitchen and, at his prompting, I clobbered him with a ladle and raised great saucer-like purple bruises on his upper arm and thigh. I felt terrible. But, to be honest, there was something exciting about that little taste of violence.

His health was a concern. I'd not have thought it possible, but he got skinnier and paler. What I'd put down to diet and indoor living started to look like a serious illness. But as soon as I touched on the subject, he went to get a blood test for pretty much every communicable disease on the planet, bringing back a clean bill of health, which he seemed to think closed the discussion. I took to bringing pastries whenever we met but gave up on the idea when I ate three eclairs unassisted.

There was always a bit of a block between us when it came to conversation, but I learned to find the difference in our outlooks funny.

'I'm working with this Japanese tea company,' I might say. 'I'm trying to come up with an English name for their beverages. What do you think about Fidelitea?'

He just wondered why anyone would spend five dollars on a drink that was so easy to make yourself; the seas were choking on plastic bottles.

We trundled along in this manner for some time, with Soren becoming a regular intermission in my life. I adored those crystal-blue eyes and that tender, slightly ugly body, its pallor and slenderness at odds with his stature. There was no time to see anyone else, and frankly there was so much intensity and passion in Soren, I didn't feel the need. The difference between us had come to be a draw for me, like visiting a foreign country. To ask for him to be less strange, more like me, would be like visiting the Amazon and pining for a Starbucks.

Then came a long period of absence, perhaps three months. There was no explanation, when normally I'd get a text that he was up at the Finger Lakes, at the commune. With him gone so long, my compass was spinning; I felt lost. Then one day he reached out to tell me he'd be going upstate and would be gone a long time. There was no suggestion we should meet. The Finger Lakes were meant to be beautiful, and to my surprise I'd really come to miss him, so I offered to drive. He said that would be helpful.

When I picked him up, he looked worse than ever. His collarbone was jutting out, and the circles around his eyes were blue-black.

'You need to see a doctor and get off that awful, stupid diet,' I said.

But he just reeled off a litany of environmental horrors: Siberian tundra on fire; rainforests levelled; seas acidifying. He said the oceans were losing their capacity to store carbon, which has been slowing down the effects of climate change; and they also produce two-thirds of the world's oxygen, without which large mammalian life won't be able to survive.

'You can't hope to remedy any of that if you're just wasting away.'

He laughed, scornful and sad. After that, he slept through the whole five-hour drive.

It's hard for me to describe the commune at the Finger Lakes, because for most of my stay one giant word was flashing red across my mind's eye: BEDBUGS. To be fair, the place was very clean. Someone was always busy doing the housework, which was shared. But people there dressed like the homeless. They might have been trying to advertise how contemptuous they were of appearances, which is pretty vain in itself.

There was one big house and some little cottages scattered around. When we entered the main living space, about half a dozen people mobbed Soren as if he were a conquering hero. I made myself scarce, retreating to an Airbnb I'd booked earlier. I was disappointed when Soren said he was too tired to join me. I'm in shape and fairly easy on the eye, and from a man in his early thirties that kind of demurral would normally sound the alarm. But Soren could barely stand for five minutes, and he looked genuinely apologetic.

Cassia, a woman from the commune, visited me that evening. She found me in the only passable restaurant in town.

'Girlfriend or fiancée?' I asked, bracing myself. 'I don't think Soren would cheat on a wife.'

She shook her head and frowned; my deduction was clearly way off target.

I offered to buy her a drink, but she declined and started telling me about Soren's interest in Buddhism and the time he'd spent in Japan at a Shingon monastery. The Shingon monks take asceticism to an extreme that many people consider deranged, but Soren was fascinated. Hundreds of years ago, the founding patriarch of this monastic school had brought back a practice from China called *Sokushinbutsu*, a tantric ritual that takes a minimum of three years and which is not only thought to bring enlightenment but to leave the body in a state that serves as a reminder to others that spiritual strength can overcome any demand of the physical realm.

Her description of Sokushinbutsu was very abstract, and it was clear she was tiptoeing around the big reveal.

'I've seen what Soren eats and how little,' I said. 'It's killing him. So, I hope he's almost done with this stupid ritual.'

In a manner of speaking, he was almost done, she explained. His diet was designed to minimise the amount of fat in the body. The pine needles he ate deposited traces of resin in the flesh. In the final stage of the ritual, Soren would stop eating altogether and drink a special tea made from tree bark, the source of Japanese lacquer, which contains the same toxin found in poison ivy. This would make the body inhospitable to bacteria and would, as she put it, ease him through the final stages.

'Final stages of what?' I said, starting to feel nauseous.

At the end of Sokushinbutsu, the monk descends into a pit three metres deep. He climbs into a pine casket packed around with charcoal (Cassia's voice started to crack). Then the casket is sealed up and buried. Rising to the surface is a breathing tube and a string attached to a bell.

'How long does a monk stay down there?'

Long after the bell stops ringing, she said. Three years longer, to be exact, after which the monk is exhumed and, if everything went well, with the deterioration of fats and the introduction of tannins into the flesh, his body will have become mummified, a testament to the soul's triumph over the trials of this world.

I ordered a Stoli, pronto.

'That's not what Soren's going to do?'

But she nodded, very grim, telling me how he'd said I had been kind to him and deserved the truth. He hoped I'd understand that this was a protest, a gesture designed to wake people from their apathy to the damage being done to the planet.

Soren had been preparing himself for more than three years, slowly reducing his intake of nutrients, ridding himself of the fats that decomposed fastest in a corpse. He was very weak now. Within three or four weeks, he would be buried alive.

There was no police station for miles around. The next day, I put in a call to 911, but found it hard to explain a tantric ritual of starvation to the dispatcher. I was told a patrol car would, at some point, visit the commune. Knowing how little this meant, I drove back to New York in tears, a danger to traffic. As well as sad, I was angry that a man with so much to offer would throw his life away.

My feelings developed over the next week or so. Soren wasn't hurting anyone, and perhaps his gesture would be meaningful. I toyed with the idea that it was a triumph of the will, a source of inspiration. For the next two weeks, I was crushing it at the gym every single day, pushing myself harder than I'd ever thought possible. When pilates or yoga ended, I went straight to the cardio room. An instructor named me Joan of Arc Trainers. I was ripped like a gymnast. Yoga gear became my uniform.

I owed it all to Soren. His otherness threw my own personality into high relief. He'd allowed me to understand myself. And he'd given me so many new statements to make on social media. Do you know that half the carbon in the atmosphere has been put there in the last thirty years, since Al Gore wrote his first book on climate change? People had started to look at me differently since I'd come to know him, and that really opened doors.

Had Soren actually gone through with that crazy ritual? I'd texted him, but he never replied. In the end, about a month after my trip to the Finger Lakes, I decided to go back there. I was scared of what I would find, but I had to know.

Once at the commune, I was left alone in the common area of the central building until Cassia arrived, the community's ambassador. She looked drawn and fatigued. Very firmly, but not unkind, she told me to go home. There was no point in my being there. Soren was beyond anyone's assistance, but he could still be perturbed. I think that was how she put it.

'He's been buried, hasn't he?' I said, fingers clamped over my mouth in horror.

She nodded.

'Is ... the bell still ringing?'

Another nod.

Eventually, I prevailed. Tears didn't work, but I threatened to stay indefinitely and make a nuisance of myself, to call the police and generally spread the news that the commune was helping a man commit suicide. Having extracted a promise not to talk about what was going on until the time Soren was exhumed, she led me out across a field. A light mist hung about the distant wood where we were heading. The path between the trees was marked out with cairns and graced with wooden steps leading to the top of a bare hill. There, beneath a gazebo weaved together from untreated branches a bell was mounted on a post. Beside it a plastic tube the size of a sink's drain protruded from the freshly broken earth.

The bell tinkled. Soren was alive, perhaps even aware, deep below, that he had visitors.

Cassia retreated a few feet as I kneeled at the breathing tube conscious of being observed. It dawned on me only now that Soren was beyond rescue. I was here, I understood at last, to say goodbye. And, so, I spoke to him through the drainpipe, and as I did so my heart lifted out of my body.

'It's Joan. I want to tell you something. You've taken me on an amazing journey.' My voice was clear and strong, though the tears were flowing. 'I've been somewhere I never knew existed: to the inner parts of myself. There's something about you that's opened up a world of possibilities. I can't tell you how much I've achieved in the office in the past few weeks, how hard I've been working out, how strong I feel – and I'm going to keep it up, I'm going to live a more vital, productive life and realise my full potential, in my career and otherwise. It's all thanks to you. I understand how much I want a family now, a big one. And you know what else? I came up with a name for that Japanese tea company: it's going to be called Greenest Teas. The name keys into environmental themes, which are resonating really powerfully with all our focus groups right now. The logo is going to be a bell – yes, like this one – in tribute to you, and your story is going to be the secret narrative to all our marketing, helping it to get picked up on all kinds of platforms. Next week I'm flying out to Sydney for a conference about environmental choices in consumerism. And I'm getting a cat. I've even got this amazing robot thing to keep it company while I'm away. Getting to know you has been life-changing. Thanks to you, I'm attuned to nature like never before.'

After that, there was only silence. It was early evening. Shadows creeped from under the trees. I stayed on my knees until the chill had worked its way under my sweater. Cassia led me back to the commune and my car, not saying a word, too overcome with emotion to look me in the eye.

The bell didn't ring again.

Last Orders at the Café Fledermaus

Kahn & Selesnick

One evening, Orlofsky had me meet him at a local restaurant called Lulu's for a bit of dinner prior to our final performance at the Academy. Upon arriving, I found him in a greater state of agitation than was usual; I felt disinclined to indulge him, but he grabbed my hand passionately and pleaded with me to stay. The proprietress crossed the room bearing a platter of junipered lamb in truffled cream curds. Orlofsky at once became so excited that I feared he would make a spectacle of himself, strange given that he knew I loathed this dish. Then I realised: it was not the dish that had excited him, but rather the woman carrying it. How disappointingly banal! Sensing my disapproval, he calmed down and told me to be patient: I was about to undergo a remarkable transformation. I did not like the smirk that crossed his face when he made this last statement. Annoyed, I reached for the menu. As I pretended to study its contents an unpleasant reek began to pervade the air – an intense odour of sour milk with an underlayer not dissimilar to the stink of the monkey-house or farmyard, but also undercut with something beyond definition, perhaps the malevolent sweetness of angels. Lulu herself, evidently the source of this odour, stood before me with a notepad. As the smell penetrated my lungs, I became overwhelmed, and the words on the menu started to spin and dissolve until they exploded altogether and I was somewhere else entirely, some*thing* else entirely: I was a mighty stink-deer in the rotting, damp boreal forests of the North; boiling steam poured off my rank haunches as I lumbered

[191]

through a marshy under-litter of huge decaying logs covered in jack-moss and sphagnum. An enormous rut was upon me, and I could smell the acrid stench of the she-buck through the matted fur of my heaving muzzle; to relieve my wretched ecstasy I reared up on my hind hooves and let out a fearsome bellow that echoed deep into silent conifers. The restaurant was silent, and everyone was staring in our direction. I was standing, even though I had no clear recollection of having stood up. Had I bellowed aloud? Looking down, I realised that I had clearly embarrassed myself and a hasty exit was in order. Orlofsky was in a giddy stupor; I grabbed him by the scruff of the neck, slapped some bills on the table, and stumbled into the cold night air.

It was a while before I felt myself again. We had missed our performance once more – another bridge burned, but what was to be done? It seemed, though, that another door had opened in spectacular fashion. As we wandered the avenues, I recalled reading about the great smell armies of Babylon, who could nauseate or intoxicate their opponents at will, or produce complex odours capable of inducing such intense olfactory nostalgia that opposing armies would simply lay down their weapons and return home to their wives or mothers, often in tears over long vanished summers or childhoods. And what of the rumoured smell museum of the Three Kingdoms Dynasty, hidden deep within the forbidden city before its destruction by revolutionaries, said to have contained every possible aroma, including some now unknown to us, the legendary smells of heaven. But then who was to say that there were not government sponsored aroma-agents among us already; after all, hadn't a Tewkesbury Stilton supposedly caused the Rape of Neumarket in 1814? I thought back to the incident at Lulu's: such an olfactory assault was almost tantamount to an act of aggression. We were lucky to have survived, things could have been far worse. Perhaps the real answer lay in the purchase of a stout deodorant, inexpensively obtained at the local pharmacy, available in either spray or roll-on form...

Kahn & Selesnick
Last Orders at the Café Fledermaus

Whenever I film anything, I feel less lonely

In February 2020, as the pandemic was looming, I found myself driving aimlessly across the High Desert in Oregon. Teeming with life and biodiversity and encompassing a rich history of Native cultures, deserts are also seen as tabula rasas – blank spaces where mystics, healers, prophets and even Gods have traditionally gone to wrestle with the ineffable. *We Shall All Be Healed* tells the story of how one scientist's encounter with the desert leads him to a new understanding of the world and the mysterious forces that govern it. These images are shots from the film with narration overlaid as text.

Kevin Bell
Rest Area, Oil on canvas

Kevin Bell
Dam, Oil on canvas

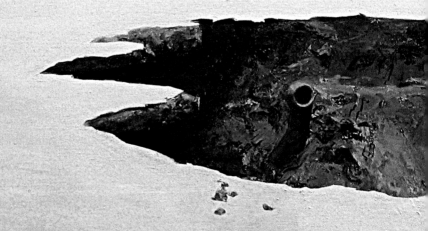

Caroline Ross
Hermit, Irongall ink on deer parchment,
drawn with goose feather, 2020

The Light in the Trees

Paul Kingsnorth

The girl picked her way carefully across the limestone fissures. The dog had gone ahead of her as usual, following a zagging path with ease into the low hazel scrub that dusted the edge of the mountain. The sky was a skulking, dirty ivory. She moved slowly. It would be easy to twist an ankle here, and hard to hobble the distance to the nearest house.

When she reached the low wall that separated his small kingdom from the world outside, she hesitated. She was never sure quite whether to walk across. There was a right of way alright. It was owned by the tourist board or the heritage council or something, the whole place. It wasn't as if it belonged to him. For a moment, the girl resented him for her hesitation. He acted like he owned the place. Or was it her who acted as if he did?

The dog was sitting next to him where he knelt. It had been drinking from the well again; drops of clear mountain water admixed with saliva were dripping from its stupid mouth. The dog smiled at her fulsomely, and she scowled. It had no sense of the sacred, this dog. She was embarrassed on its behalf. But the man did not react to either of them. She could hear him praying as he knelt by the spring. He seemed uninterested in her, or the dog, though she could tell some-how that he knew she stood there behind him, hovering, uncertain. The words came steadily, repeated and repeated.

Lord Jesus Christ, son of God, have mercy on me, a sinner.
Lord Jesus Christ, son of God, have mercy on me, a sinner.

The first time she'd seen him doing this she'd almost turned around and never come back. Jesus: she'd had a childhood full of him, full of communions, masses, confirmations, they all merged into one, and Jesus was responsible for all of them. She hadn't been to church since. Her mam refused to go at all now, after everything that had happened, even to the adoration when the pews were mostly empty. Whatever Jesus might actually have been saying had been drowned out long ago and the girl was still getting her breath back.

She hadn't walked that first time, though, because she had found the prayer so unexpectedly mesmerising. She had forgotten that prayer could do this. She stood listening now, and after a while the words merged into a stream and lost their meaning and became an elongated drone, punctuated by a dissonant, repeating *ssss*, steadily beating like a thin drum over the hill. *s-s-s, ss-ss. s-s-s, ss-ss.* It went on like that until she felt she was falling into the sound, and the hazel scrub and the limestone bluff and the cave mouth retreated and only the sound remained. No Jesus, no sinners, no mountain, no dog. Only the sound, rolling like pasture. *s-s-s, ss-ss.*

Then the sound stopped and everything snapped disappointingly back into place. The man stood stiffly and unfurled his long body back into the clearing like a bracken shoot. He turned to her.

Lydia, he said. *Have you seen the light in the trees?*

The girl was always taken aback by his complete lack of interest in small talk. Where she came from it was all small talk. Everybody smiled and said *how are you?* and everybody said *fine*, and under no circumstances was anybody to answer the actual question. Under no circumstances was anybody to say, *my wife just left me and I feel suicidal,* or *I'm in the depths of a rolling existential crisis,* or *I feel fantastic because I just got away with embezzling some company money.* Everybody said *fine,* and then they talked about the weather or the traffic jams on the roundabout.

I did, she said, a bit.

A bit?

I did, but not as bright as before, but deeper, somehow, and longer. I was walking home again from the shop, down past the new estate, there are lime trees there in a line, and—

And?

He would always prompt her like this, as if from the wings, as if she were standing in the spotlight dried up and shamed. He was like an arrow heading directly for…well, what? What exactly? All she knew was how to answer, which is what she supposed she had come for.

Last time, she said, last time – the first time – when we talked about it – that time I was looking out of my bedroom window at home. I told you, you remember? I was looking out of the window, I wasn't looking for anything, and I saw the trees all shift. I saw it out of the corner of my eye, and then I looked at them directly and all the trees were glowing. It was like they were dancing, they were glowing gold, like they weren't trees at all but were made of gold dust and light. It only lasted a few seconds and then it all snapped back to normal. You remember I told you?

Keep going.

And I thought maybe it was just a trick of the light or something, but you said—

I said it was the first stage and that it would happen again. And now it has. What did you see this time, Lydia?

Like I said, it was different trees. Limes. Or maybe poplars. No, limes, because poplars are thinner aren't they? Taller. Anyway. I was just walking past and I saw the flicker again and I looked up. It was a deeper gold colour this time. They didn't shimmer, but it was like I was looking through them. Like they were not trees at all but just patterns. Geometric patterns. And I felt that – I don't know—

What did you feel?

I felt they weren't trees at all. No, not that. I mean, I felt like they were there, but they weren't all that they were. I didn't feel it, I saw it. That's what I mean, I think. Ah, it's impossible! It was just – it was like they were all bundled up by some pattern of thread to the sky and the ground, and the sky and the ground weren't there either as I always thought, they were just words, and—

The man smiled, for the first time since she had arrived. She liked the deep clefts that appeared on either side of his eyes, and the way that the smile always reached every part of his face.

The cure for all confusion, he said, *is coffee. Saint Seraphim said that. Or if he didn't, he should have done.*

He had a fire down from the cave mouth that always seemed to be alight. He had once told her that coffee was his only vice, but there was a twinkle in his eyes when he had said it, and she wasn't sure what he meant by vice, anyway. He didn't look like someone who had ever had any vices, had ever been anywhere but here, in this small wood, under the cave mouth, in the ruins of the old church. He looked like he had sprouted from the mulch of hazel leaves and moss that bearded the spring as it emerged from the face of the mountain.

Father – she said.

I told you not to call me that.

I can't help it. What should I call you, then?

You don't have to call me anything.

Everyone needs a name.

I used to have a name. God took it away because it didn't serve him anymore. If he wants to give me another one I suppose he will, but what would I do with it? Nothing here needs a word for me.

What was your name? The girl felt she was taking a risk. She had known the man for two months or so now, since she had first walked into the woods with the dog and seen him outside the cave. She had known this place for years, but she had never seen anyone staying here before. It had been obvious he had moved in though, even though he had brought virtually nothing with him: a sleeping bag, a coffee pot, a small rucksack. Bearded, unwashed, he could have been anyone from any city doorway, but he wasn't that and she had known it right away. A hermit had lived in this cave once, centuries ago. He had built a little stone church here, which had long fallen in on itself. The embers glowed where the altar had been. She knew nothing about him at all, and had never asked. This was the first time, and she didn't know what the reaction would be.

If God took it away it means he doesn't want me to use it any more.

Did God bring you here?

I suppose so.

Where were you before?

The man looked at her intently. His eyes were like those of a bird, now, she thought. His beard was white, with yellow-brown stains around the mouth, it straggled down below his neckline and only his hawkish nose and pale blue eyes could be seen above it. He poured the coffee into two dirty tin mugs and handed one to the girl.

Around, he said. *It's not important. What is important is that it will happen again. Each time it has happened to you there has been a shift, a deepening, yes?*

Yes, said the girl, quietly. She sipped the coffee and felt restless and echoing, like a deep sea trench.

Each time it happens the world is precisely the same afterwards in all of its particulars, but something in the way that you see it has changed. You cannot put your finger on it, you cannot put it into words, but everything is different, though also the same, and you can never reach again the place you stood in just five minutes before, and you are not the same person who stood there. Is that how it is?

The girl wanted to say nothing, but she nodded slightly against herself. The man drew a mouthful of coffee and swallowed.

It will happen again, Lydia, because you are being drawn. God is pulling you towards himself. He has something to show you.

Who said I even believed in God?

It felt like a bold thing to say, but the girl could feel the resistance growing in her. He always had to know everything. She needed what he had to say, because only he seemed to know what was going on with her, and yet some part of her rebelled every time. Now something in what he'd said had stuck into her like a thorn and she was aggravated in some place she couldn't reach.

Do you go to church? he asked.

No, she said. I hate church. It doesn't say anything to me.

Ah, said the man, resting the mug of coffee on his knee. *Well, that's good.* The girl glanced sideways at him, expecting something more, but he just sat looking into the embers.

You talk about God, she said. How do you know there is one?

The thing about the church, said the man, as if he hadn't heard, *is that it talks about God as if he lived somewhere else. Up there, in some place we can't see. As if he'd issued a list of rules to follow and then disappeared, and you get to find out after you're dead whether you got the instructions right. Don't you find?*

I suppose, said the girl. Suddenly she felt that she wanted to go home. Where was the dog? She wanted to go home, now. The man placed his coffee cup by the embers and stood up slowly, as if he was trying not to break something.

All I know, he said, *is that when God gets hold of you, he shakes you like a dog with a rat. He shakes you until your guts are on the floor. He turns you inside out and then sets you down hollow and nothing that once mattered means anything at all. Then he tells you what you're really here for.*

The girl put her cup down and started to rise too.

At least, said the man, *that's how it seems to me.*

[198]

Lydia, would you serve this customer?

The girl hated having to wear a mask at work. Apart from the discomfort, it meant that the customers couldn't see whether she was smiling at them or not. She felt it was important to smile, and not just because this was her first ever job. She thought that perhaps, like the man, they would see the smile in her eyes.

Some of the customers wore masks and others didn't. A month or two ago, everyone had been stockpiling toilet roll and hectoring each other about social distancing on their Facebook pages, but now they were getting bored. People got bored easily, the girl had noticed. One week they were all furious about some urgent global cause, the next they'd gone back to sharing gifs of dancing animals. This week, the consensus seemed to be that the viral apocalypse had been prevented by all the hashtags and stockpiling, and that everything would be back to normal soon. The girl didn't think anything would ever be normal again. She had seen the light in the trees.

Can you put a new battery in this watch for me? said the customer, a young man without a mask. Young men never wore masks, she had noticed, and they didn't often say please either. She looked at the watch, which was flashy but cheap.

Of course, sir, she said, smiling, hoping he would notice the eyes. Can you pop back in about half an hour?

She wrote his name on a tag, attached it to the watch and then headed in the direction of the back room, where Kenneth sat before a pile of watches in need of repair. As she took hold of the door handle, everything dissolved.

Just like that, it happened. The girl didn't know where she stood or what supported her body or if she even had one. It was as if everything had gone. She had been glancing casually at the glass showcase of jewelled earrings and necklaces, and they had just slid away, it seemed, slid away into nothing: the glass, the jewellery, the lot. Something was still there – something existed – but it wasn't the shop or the door handle or the earrings or Kenneth or Lydia. The world had rearranged itself into a vast array of patterns, shades and shapes, towering above her and disappearing beneath into chambers and chimneys of light and sound, great echo soundings of love and distance.

She knew then that all of this had been there all the time, behind everything she walked through, that this was the true shape of the world, or the primal shape, or something. As usual, her understanding collapsed as soon as she tried to lock it down with words, so she stopped herself and just stood wherever it was she was standing, watching the shapes and colours spiral back into infinity, watching the crystalline mountains and waterfalls of light and not being quite sure who watched any of it or what would happen next.

Lydia!

Kenneth happened next. He came out of the door she had been about to open, and nearly knocked her to the floor. The floor was there again suddenly, normal had returned, the waterfalls and caverns and patterns were gone as if they had never been, and Kenneth was apologising for not looking where he was going. She was suddenly filled with love for Kenneth. He was the kind of person who apologised when somebody else stepped on his foot or took his place in a queue. Everybody should be like Kenneth. The universe was made up of patterns like Kenneth, patterns of love and apology, or at least that was how they started out, but most of them got corrupted by what we thought reality was, and now here we all were, hashtagging and stockpiling and fighting over stories. The girl didn't know what she was talking about or what anything meant or how she was going to get through to five o'clock with this great burden of love suddenly exploding from her, suddenly arrowing at her from all directions, suddenly weighing her down and forcing her to swim out far away from the shore.

It was dusk when she arrived at the low wall. She hadn't brought the dog this time. She didn't want to be distracted. She felt ashamed now of the state she had got herself into last time. She remembered what the man had said about God shaking people like rats and wondered if this was what he had meant. Once you had seen the caverns and the waterfalls, what were you to do with the world? He would know. If he didn't know, there was only catastrophe coming for her.

He wasn't in the clearing this time. She could hear no prayers. She walked over to the church ruin, which looked gloomier in the fading light. The fire was out. She had never seen his fire out, but the embers were black and cold. Suddenly panicked, she walked faster up the slope to the cave mouth. His sleeping bag was gone. She ran back down to the clearing. There was no sign of him here at all. No rucksack, no sleeping bag, no coffee pot, no sense of his presence anywhere.

She wanted to call his name, but she didn't know it. Hello! she shouted into the gloom. Hello? Nothing. Even the birds were still with the sinking of the sun. The only sound was the trickle and bubble from the stream as it was born from the foot of the mountain.

He wasn't here. He had gone.

The girl hadn't cried for years, not like this, but as she walked back across the limestone she couldn't stop herself. The tears ran down her neck and soaked into her shirt. She was coursed by sobs that felt as uncontrollable as her visions. Everything was lost. He had talked to her about what she saw when she had nobody else to tell, and now, with everything hanging like a thin moon in winter, he had gone, gone and left her to break apart alone. She needed someone to carry her and she had nobody at all.

She reached the car, opened the door and sat behind the wheel, her hands uncontrollable. She drew deep breaths and waited for the tears to end and the sobbing to crest and fall away. She gripped the wheel, closed her eyes, focused on her breathing. She felt like the waters of the ocean in the passing of a storm

When she opened her eyes it was almost dark outside. She could barely see the mountain. She thought she could make it home now. She would focus on the road. She had only been driving for a few months, since her sixteenth birthday, and she needed to be clear in her head, especially at night. Driving at night could be hypnotic, especially in lonely places like this. But she wanted to be hypnotised now and never wake up. She started the engine and moved off slowly, watching the headlights sweep over the stone walls like a lighthouse beam and curved away.

It was less than five minutes before the car stopped. She was driving carefully around a series of corkscrew bends spiralled with hazel and outcrops of rock like broken teeth, when the engine coughed several times, stuttered and died away. The car rolled to a stop by the roadside. The girl threw her hands in the air, stifled a scream, looked instinctively at the fuel gauge. Empty. Frustration took hold and began to melt swiftly into fear. This morning, the universe had been full of love; it had been built from it like brick and she had wanted to live in it and preach it to everyone she saw, to hymn it in all the notes that were ever made. This evening, it was revealed as cold and unforgiving of any human notion.

Perhaps she had misunderstood everything. She wished she had never come here at all. What would mum and dad think when she didn't come back? She only wanted to be at home, in front of the TV, with their voices murmuring in the kitchen. She wanted never to have started driving, working, anything. She wanted to cancel her adulthood right here. She wanted to be further away from herself than it was ever possible to be.

The door opened and the man got in and sat in the passenger seat beside her. He looked at her intently as he pulled the door closed, as if to gauge her condition.

What? she said. Where—

I told you, he said, *do you remember? Nothing that once mattered means anything at all. Does it feel like that?*

Go away, she said. Get out of my car. Where were you? What are you doing here? Do you know what I saw?

She looked over at him. She saw the lines at the edge of his eyes again. His beard looked even messier than usual.

I will go if you want me to, he said. *Of course.* He waited for a response. The girl stared at the steering wheel. The headlights were still on, illuminating a barbed wire fence and a field of rush wandering out beyond.

Say the Jesus Prayer with me, said the man, after a minute. *It's easy. You've heard it before.*

I don't want to.

What you want has very little to do with anything at this point, said the man.

I told you, I don't like any of this stuff.

I know. Think of it as a mantra, if you prefer. Just a sound. Certain sounds have certain results. Just make the sound and keep making it and we'll see what happens, shall we?

Do I have to?

You don't have to do anything. You came to find me, remember. All of this is your doing.

The girl said nothing because there was nothing to say other than Get out of my car or OK then, and she didn't want to say either of them.

Lord Jesus Christ, said the man, *Son of God, have mercy on me, a sinner.* He said it quietly and then said it again. He said it four times and then he kept saying it, each time deepening it somehow, sinking it down into a place beyond his presence, each time increasing the volume slightly so that it filled the car without being loud or obtrusive. *s-s-s, ss-ss. s-s-s, ss-ss.* After a minute, the girl began to join in, hesitantly, annoyed at first and then embarrassed but then, realising he was not listening, realising she was not being judged, with more intent, until she felt her voice deepening too and filling the space and moving up and out and below and beyond. *s-s-s, ss-ss. s-s-s, ss-ss.*

And then she felt it happening again. Not instantly this time but more steadily, gradually, as if she were being given a chance to turn and run, a chance to sit up and say Stop! and go home instead and feed the dog. She stayed with it. *s-s-s, ss-ss. s-s-s, ss-ss.* The sound filled the car and the road and the landscape until there was no car or road or landscape or anything at all, but his voice was still there, she could still hear him and he had stopped praying now and everything that had been rhythm was now silence and plain. She saw the crystals again and the rivers of time and all of the angles and multiples rainbowed into everything in ways that could not be communicated.

Welcome to the Kingdom of God, said the man's voice.

It's what I saw this morning, she said. She heard her own words but saw nothing of herself or him. She knew she was being watched and that she always had been. There was a presence, behind her and all around her, and she was afraid and not afraid at all.

The what?

The Kingdom of God. This is what we call it, anyway. It has other names. I expect the church told you you would get to it after you died if you apologised enough.

What is it?

It's just the world. The world in its perfection. You were always here, but you never saw, because you were never looking. This is the state of humanity, we walk through paradise with our eyes shut. But it's all around you, all of the time. Here you are, and there is no you and that is all of the secret. You were never born, you never die, everything is in you and you are in everything. It is all just as it was when you walked to me over the stones. Nothing has changed at all except the way you see it.

Everything was flickering then, everything was illuminated, and whatever the great presence was it was one she had felt before, perhaps forever, only through some veil, some curtain, some glass.

Do you see how the threads connect it all? said the man. *When I first saw it I nearly died. The lights in the trees are the lights in your eyes. When your mind takes the world apart to learn what it is, all that it learns is the anxiety of separation. We call this the Fall. And when you see that there is no mind and no parts and no you that was ever born or will ever die, when you see that death is not possible and that you are every creature that moves and beats in time, then you are back in the Garden. Then you are everything there is. That's the Kingdom of God.*

The girl said something in reply, but she wasn't sure what it was. She could see nothing, even her own body. The universe was obstructing her view.

At least, said the man, *that's how it seems to me.*

How did I get here? asked the girl.

You died.

You mean—

I mean you died. Not your body. Your body is still in the driver's seat. Snap your fingers and you'll see the headlights and the wire again, just as it was. What died was your self, your will, your ego, and just for a moment. Your self gets in the way of reality, you see. Your small worlds, your little truths that are not truths, the temptations, the opinions, the striving. They have to die for you to see. To see the Kingdom, you must give up all of your ideas about what the world is. That's what they were supposed to teach you in church: how to die.

The girl stared at everything at once and it all seemed to stare back.

Die to your self, rise again, serve the world, said the man. *That's the Jesus bit. It's why nobody likes it.*

So what is it? said the girl. The normal stuff, I mean. The everyday things. What's happening?

My conclusion, said the man, *is that everything you see every day, everyone you know, everything around you: all of it is made by your mind. None of it has any substance unless you believe it does. You created the mountain, the cave, your place of work. You created me. We create our own little worlds and we carry them on our backs like sacks of winter wood. Once they break and fall away, there is reality, waiting for you. Sometimes, for some lucky people like you, the breaks can happen with no work on your part. But most of the time, the false world doesn't die on its own. We have to kill it. That's the work. That's the long, long work.*

My world, said the girl. I made it?

You made it, said the man. *Your fears, your anger, your needs, your passions, your desires: they made it all. Everything you see is what you need to see. It's like a series of clues, I think, clues that you have to find. When you finally escape, you see this. This is the real world. This is the Kingdom.*

But what do I do with it? said the girl. What do I do now?

It's not what you do with it, said the man's voice. *It's what it does with you.*

The girl felt some shiver pass through her body, though she didn't know where her body was or what was watching or speaking. Everything shimmered for a second.

He has something to show you, said the man's voice again. And then suddenly it was gone, everything was gone, the voice, the kingdom, everything dropped away as it had done in the shop and the girl was back in the car, as if no time had passed or years had passed.

Outside, the headlights were still illuminating the wire and the scrub. Was that an owl? She thought she heard an owl pass over.

There was nobody in the passenger seat.

The girl peered straight ahead of her, screwing up her eyes so that she could make out the parliament of trees assembled just beyond the reach of the beam. The silver road rolled away before her like a canyon floor. She noticed that her hands, still gripping the wheel, were shaking slightly. Everything was the same as it had always been, and everything was new.

She turned the key, started the engine and began to move slowly away down the hill.

Illustrations by **Caroline Ross**

p.193, *Tree*, Irongall ink on deer parchment, 2020
p.199, *Heath*, Irongall ink on deer buckskin, 2020
p.207, *Cliff*, Irongall ink on deer buckskin, 2020

All the skins were saved from burial as waste, and dehaired, stretched and / or tanned by me with entirely natural materials using traditional methods. The ink was made with foraged oak galls, cherry tree gum, rusty scrap iron and rainwater. The drawings were created using pens and brushes made from feathers moulted from local geese. I used the markings on the skin caused by how it grew, the life of the animal, or the traces left by tools in tanning the hide, to suggest first marks for these landscape works. These pictures were then sent to the writer, for him to respond to in words.

The Gramarye

Kirsty Logan

i first see Him in the rain & the daisies say yes—
i am at the window sighing & praying for i know not what plagues
me—

its my sins i suppose with girls its always their sins what ever those
sins might be well you know with a girl theres always a sin or two
floating around—

i dont know the nature of my plague i know only that i am
plagued—

the voices of my sisters in song only angers me & bores me which
i know is not my own voice & my own thoughts because i have taken
vows & that surely makes me holy in word & thought & deed—

my thoughts may not be holy & my words when i say them inside
my own head are not at all holy—

my deeds though must seem holy as unholy means witch & witch
means drowned & burned—

but the vows will fix my sinful thoughts for me i think because god
loves a sinner & i think often of sin & i hope that makes him love me
more—

only one window looks out to the walls & the bridge & the river
& the road & the woods beyond—

all the other windows look into the courtyard but one window a
secret little small one thats up a tower & awkward you have to climb
unladylike & tip your self so any one who might be coming up the
stairs would see the unholy thing under your skirt & become unholy
by the sight of it so theyd better not come up the stairs is all i will say

about it because i come up to the window as often as i can—

   & by the way the windows are set like that so that we dont look out of them & look always in wards in to our thoughts & not out wards to the world & its sinful etceteras so perhaps my vows would work better if i did not look out of the window so much i dont know—

   outside the window the rain comes slow then quick quiet then loud thrumming spitting—

   the daisies are out it is summer—

   always it is summer—

   the days long slow hazy endless—

   tomorrow the same & yesterday & the next & before—

   the air still holds the heat of the sun—

   the rain falls hard & i put out my hand lean out of the window far so i might fall so i can touch the rain but i do not fall—

   the daisies in the rain nod yes—

   & i see Him walk by along the river & the rain does not bother Him at all His head high His eyes deep in thought of good pure holy glowing things & i want that to be me good pure holy glowing me & the good pure world i can show Him & the good pure light of my love for Him—

   & the rain wet on my hands & i lean out so far my feet come up off the floor & i look down on Him passing & i nod yes i will have that one yes—

   & He keeps walking—

   & the rain falls—

   & the daisies nod yes yes yes—

———

   i first see Him soothing the bees—

   some of the bees the ones in the sixth hive have gone mad & father fleck says they are possessed by demons—

which may be true because i suppose any thing might be true god
has his ways & means—

all we know the girls & i—

thats me & jennet issobel grissel marion agnes gilleis lizabet alizon
jehan hanna isidore oh & euphemia thats every one i think—

all we know is that the five hives of bees are fine & friends & so
any one of us can go & collect the honey with the mask & every
thing of course because they may be friends but they are still bees &
bees have stings we must not forget the true nature of things suchlike
as bees are full of stings & women are full of sins—

though mostly He collects the honey because the bees like Him
best which makes me not surprised because i also like Him best—

He goes to collect the honey from the sixth hive & the bees all of a
sudden possessed bewitched mad with sin & lust & anger the bees
swarm at Him try to get inside His mask to sting Him—

& i cant help but think they only want to kiss Him & i understand
i know bees i feel the same i want to swarm & kiss & bring honey to
His lips—

but when He tells father fleck about the bees we—

thats me & jennet issobel grissel marion agnes gilleis lizabet alizon
jehan hanna isidore oh & euphemia—

we all hear because girls have big ears & we are glad to hear
because we are all too frightened to collect the honey because of the
mad bees but father fleck needs the honey to sell to travellers &
visitors who come passing by so the church can be kept up & so that
we can etcetera have food to eat—

so father fleck says it is an unsatisfactory situation & the bees must
be exorcised & father fleck tells Him to do it at once—

& He does the exorcisms mostly women of course but also
chickens dogs goats frogs horses geese & once a caterpillar that kept
eating the lettuces so of course bees are fine for Him—

we all have work to do we have to collect the eggs & milk the cows
& suchlike but i get gilleis to do my chores because i did hers once

[211]

when she had her blood & was dirty & didnt want to taint the food with her sins so i creep to the window & watch—

i watch as He in His layers of white wound round His body like Hes made of light—

i watch as He picks up the sixth beehive the hive full of mad bees & right away they swarm out & onto Him He is covered in a twitching raging black mass & the hum is so loud like a pain in my head but He is calm as if He is covered only in butterflies or feathers soft things stroking things singing Him soft songs—

& He carries the beehive away from the others—

far far away from the animals & from us—

He takes the beehive right over the bridge over the river all the way to where the trees start—

He sets the beehive down in the shadows there—

& He takes off His white things & He is far away & small now but i still watch as He lays His small far away hands on the hive & the small far away bees calm—

they do they calm for Him not mad not possessed but calm bees now good bees holy bees—

He walks away from the calm & holy bees & He does not see me watching Him He walks in beauty the sun golden on His hair His beauty is golden sun i swoon there watching Him the heat rises up in me my desire for Him burns like a hundred hundred stings all over my body—

———

i first see Him healing jennet who is struck by fever all of a sudden—

though of course it is not fever but demons who often pretend to be other things like fever or rabbits or small black flies & it is easy for a demon to get inside a woman because they are so leaky always bleeding & milky & weepy always some thing oozing from some where so very messy—

father fleck says the demon is named asmodeus & is residing in jennets belly & father fleck tell Him to exorcise jennet so she will be well & cleansed again—

two hours it takes & i am to fetch the water always cool always fresh constant in & out to fetch water & each time i go the well handle is still warm from my hand from the last time—

father fleck there to bless the water & make it into holy water & then it can go inside jennet not all in her throat as she has already been sick a lot & theres no point putting the water in if it comes out that fast—

so it goes in all other places women as i say being leaky & oozy so things can go in & out of us very easily—

i heard of a girl who purged a live eel a foot and a half long & vomited fulsome stuff of all colours twice a day for fourteen days including hair wood pigeon dung parchment coal brass etcetera—

i heard of a girl who burned so with a fever she had a coldwater cloth on her fore head for many months to cool her brain & when it was taken away there was a bleached white patch there on her fore head which was a sign of the holy mother blessing her & i think she did die but at least she died blessed—

& now i am to help with jennets leakiness too thought i dont mind as we do help each other with suchlike things if its needed & its only a case of buckets really a lot of buckets that i empty into the river after the holy water has come back out of jennet not quite so holy—

any way this goes on for a long time i think or so it seems & i am tired of running back & forth with buckets & i think i am actually asleep while walking & i come into the dormitory & there is no thing for me to take or bring for once & it doesn't seem if jennet really knows what is happening so i dont look at her i look at Him doing the exorcism—

& its like ive never looked at a person before—

He is tired beautiful glowing head bowed as if in prayer but looking at the girl at jennet as her body arches & her breath comes fast fast fast & she lets out one final cry & i dont know what shes feeling

[213]

in her body then but i suppose it must be god & He looks at her with
total love as the demon leaves her body—
   i see His hands resting soft on jennets face—
   i see her eyes gazing up at Him—
   i see her calm she breathes slow & she slips asleep—
   & still He keeps His hand there & i think His palm is cool & good
& it would feel—
   & He is so beautiful—
   & He is so golden so good—
   & i want—
   i want—
   but theres no use in a girl wanting any thing really is there no thing
good can come of it—
   i want—

————————

This story is also available as an audio version read by the author.
See page 241 for more details, or visit dark-mountain.net/issue-18-fabula-audio

This is an excerpt from a novel in progress

The Leshy

Romy Tara Wenzel

The Leshy ate blackberries and beech nuts on the green-black moss in the long shadows of dawn. She ate the berries on their branches and the nuts inside their husks. Prickles didn't bother her. Neither did creepy-crawlies, and she swallowed the long-horned stinkbugs and the mandibled centipedes with equal appetite. She was of the Old Beings, and not much got under their skins, or upset their iron stomachs.

When the sun breached the cedar peaks, the Leshy lumbered over the forest border to the Otherside, where the four-hundred-year yew stood curled against the orange sky. If the Leshy climbed into its branches, she could see the smoke plumes curling from the village huts where the hairless ones lived. She did not climb into the branches today, but poked around the surface roots until she discovered a bundle by the badger's hole, wrapped in grey cloth. The Leshy scratched open the closure with her claws, and the cloth fell open.

The animals-without-fur often left offerings and prayers for the Leshy, twigs tied together with nettle-string to make signs the Leshy did not always understand. This piece of wood had carved paws and small round stones for eyes, its arms outstretched towards the Leshy and its knot-hole mouth open. The Leshy looked at it for a long time, furrowing her broad brow. She touched a long claw to the log, then withdrew the cloth underneath it and tucked it into a hide pouch at her hip. Turning her pelt to the thing, she loped off to the river.

A white-barked aspen had fallen in the night, blocking the path of the fish downstream. The Leshy slid into the water, wrapped her long arms around the trunk and heaved it onto the greening banks, muscles bulging in her shoulders. Fish slipped in a rush down the current, silver as molten metal. The Leshy waded in among them until the water swirled her thighs and the fish tickled her calves. She did not smile, because the Leshy never smiled, but her whiskers twitched, and her eyes half-closed like a cat.

The Leshy inspected the river for fishing lines, the eastern boundary for traps. She checked on the monarch butterflies, the last generation of their migration. She checked that the cankerworms were not over-multiplying, and ensured the woodpeckers were leaving enough acorns to mature. Last of all she lowered herself into the Circle of Bones, the moon-shaped pit littered with the femurs, spines and ribcages of animals. The Leshy lumbered over to the newest carcass. The Leshy stroked the vixen's fur, orange-gold fur and soft as it had been in life. Her stomach was round and full with the exhalations of conifer and pine as she became forest again.

The Leshy had known the vixen since she was a cub when she had come across the mother's litter in the den amongst the deep green bracken. She could still hear the cubs mewling, vividly as if the vixen were still alive. She cocked her head, remembering. Now that she thought about it, those cubs had been busy suckling at their mother's teats. This cry was new and bright as pine tips.

The Leshy slipped her long fingers underneath the bloated belly of the carcass and pulled out an orange pup, eyes squinting in the dappled light. His nostrils flared trying to catch the Leshy's scent, explored the Leshy's fingers with nose and tongue. That was how the forest-born recognised friend from foe. The animals-without-fur did not do that. They tried to catch each other with names, but the forest-born did not have names, only tastes and scents and voices.

The tiny genitals told the Leshy that this was a boy cub, far too young to be without his mother, though perhaps old enough for weaning. The Leshy heaved a sigh. That was how it was: only the strongest seedlings survived. Even the fish would have their eggs devoured, if they did not hide them in the darkest pockets of the riverbed. It had always been so. And yet, the Leshy did not put the cub down, but drew him to her chest and held him against her heartbeat. The cub pushed his nose into the Leshy's warm fur and his breaths slowed to the Leshy's breaths, in with the breeze, out with the trees.

That evening, the Leshy did not lie in the clover to listen to the moon rise. She missed the spectacle of hundreds of bats against the blue-black sky as they started their hunt, and she left the juvenile owls to their mischief. She did not patrol the eastern boundary where the poachers crossed the hunt lines. Instead she watched the sleeping fox in the crook of her arm, swaddled in the blanket she'd taken from the log-baby. Sighing, she placed the bundle by the fire and collapsed into her nest, pressing her cheek against the feather lining. She tossed and turned that night, and before the morning came, crawled over to where the fox cub lay and curled her hairy body around him.

The next morning, the Leshy did not forage for her breakfast or check the fish in the stream. She made a sling from the blanket and put the cub inside. The Leshy took long, sloping strides to the west, through the dense undergrowth and pine forest, till she reached the steppe where the trees thinned and the milk thistles prickled between the rocks.

The Leshy approached a fat grey nanny goat with silky ears, eyes like keyholes and two suckling kids. When the Leshy caught her with strong, sure hands, the goat bleated but did not run. The Leshy squeezed her milk into a waterskin, tied one end with nettle thread and bit a small hole in the other so she could squirt a thin stream from the tip. She opened the sling. The cub blinked, nosed the bladder and took suck.

When the cub's belly was round and his mouth slack, the Leshy pushed the sling to her hip, picked up the nanny in her arms and walked down the steppe. The kids followed the bleating of their mother all the way back to the Leshy's cave.

The next day, the Leshy tethered the goat to a fir-tree and did her rounds with the cub in the sling. The Leshy's long face became longer as she examined several broken branches and a disturbance in the forest floor too clumsy to be one of her animals. Growling, she undid several traps on the eastern boundary. The hairless men had crossed the unspoken line where the air greened and the shadows deepened. Several young fish floated on hooks where the poachers had left lines.

The cub was crying by the time she circled back to the yew. The Leshy sat by the badger's door to feed him. Another wooden doll lay between the tree roots, and the Leshy gazed at it as the cub sucked. It was a carefully wrought object. Birch and linen thread bound the bevelled joints. A single tear of birch-resin crept from beneath the white snail shell eyes. When the cub had finished, the Leshy tucked the fox back into its sling and took the blue swaddling. She hesitated, as if she might pick up the birch baby too, but when the howl of a wolf signalled evening the Leshy hurried back to the goats.

When the sun drew lines through the poplars and the crickets began their evensong, the Leshy smoked her pipe as she always did after the day's chores. Except she had not finished her chores. She had not finished her chores for weeks now. The fox pressed his belly against the dirt, following the smoke from the pipe, his sharp nose between his paws. The Leshy grunted and gave him a brusque pat.

The latest stick-baby watched them from the corner with its nut-husk eyes. These animals-without-fur wanted a baby, and they thought she could give them one. The Leshy knew nothing about babies. She had not been a proper baby herself, as far as she could remember, and she couldn't even look after the baby she had without the forest suffering.

The Leshy went to the village in the snap of the morning, before dawn had broken and the stars were meeting the light with violet and purple. She kept to the village path, the Worm Moon hanging low in the sky, calling up the ghost-slugs and fragile crawling things to do their work in the fallen leaves around the trees. The houses were

[218]

quiet with sleep, and the fires had died down to coals. Moonbeams streamed through the smoke-holes inside, illuminating the queer interiors.

She paused in one doorway longer than the others, examining the room. The lumps in the bed told her nothing, but on a worn table, her gaze lingered on a half-carved log, a carpenter's knife, and an assortment of stones, shells, glass and thread. The Leshy crossed the floor and transferred the sleeping fox to a basket by a spinning wheel, filled with spun wool. She looked at the faces in the bed, worn and gentle in the warming light, and then her gaze returned to the sleeping cub, his ribs rising and falling beneath the blanket. The Leshy closed her eyes and shuffled to the door. She put her hand on the doorframe, as if she would turn back. But she closed the door and vanished into the breaking day.

The Leshy finished her duties that day. She broke the cords of the hunter's lines, smashed up the twig traps and ripped up the nets. A rabbit with its leg crushed between iron jaws bleated at her, and the Leshy gently wrung the creature's neck.

She returned before the sun fell behind the western trees, ate a soup of milk-caps and nettles, filled her pipe, and watched the fire. The fire cast light and shadows on the wall of the cave while the pipe smoke smudged pictures in the air, light-play alive with possibilities. Her eyes rolled towards the empty pocket in the wall, still disturbed from where the fox had nosed out a bed.

There was no offering at the yew the next day, or the one after that. The Leshy climbed into its branches, squinting at the smoke curling from the village roofs as if she might spot the den where she had left the cub, but the roofs all looked the same, brown and relentless. The village dogs were barking in a frenzied rage, but the Leshy did not know their unwild language. The noise unnerved her, and she climbed down the tree, her claws slipping through the bark, her bones creaking.

The Leshy loped towards the kennel by the oxen pens. The dogs whined as they caught scent of her, and the Leshy stuck her snout through the fence, sniffing. The Leshy's teeth snuck under her lip as she saw the furry body curled up in a corner amongst the faeces and urine spots on the ground.

The dogs cowered as the Leshy lifted the latch and kicked open the gate. Rumbling in her throat, she scooped up her fox and nosed him. He still carried the Leshy's scent. The dogs had retreated to a far corner, fearing it. The Leshy stroked the fox's head with her thumb, and the red face pushed itself into her hand. One dog turned its nose up to howl, and the Leshy drew her claws across the dog's neck, cutting the howl short. She took the short route back through the village fields, feeling their wheat flatten beneath her feet, their vegetables squash between her toes.

That night, while the cub rolled up like a woodlouse in the Leshy's nest, the Leshy went to the eastern boundary of the forest. She did not bother taking the longer route against the wind to track them. The animals-without-fur never used their noses. She kept her steps quiet until she broke through the deerberries, and then burst through the foliage, roaring at the men who would feed her fox to their dogs. The hunters scampered away and she pounded after them, swinging a long stick at the traps to set them off as she ran past. The last man fell, and the Leshy dashed his head against a rock and threw the corpse into the goats' ravine for the vultures. After that, fewer men trespassed on the Leshy's land, but turned to setting traps for the small rats and voles that lived in their fields. The Leshy could hear the howling of the hungry dogs in the night, even from her cave.

The cub grew cunning and strong as it transitioned to red and white meat, although it remained smaller than the other forest foxes. His nose was lengthening, taking on a more vulpine shape. He explored outside the cave, disappearing while the Leshy made her rounds, dragging a pea-hen or stoat by the neck in the evening. After they shared the meal, the Leshy would smoke a pipe, and the fox would lick himself over, and then try to wash the Leshy. His barbed tongue never got further than the Leshy's feet, which were time-consuming enough.

As the light in the forest thickened and blued, the Leshy let the forest swell around her. Her mouth turned down like a salmon, and her eyes closed. Her ears, however, remained alert, swivelling this way and that to pick out one sound from another in the forest. The forest was full of magical, reassuring sounds, sounds that told her all was well and her day-work done. The whispering canopy, the last calls of the birds. To the north, the black bear rambling through fresh undergrowth. The burbling of the river, the ducks calling over the water. She pricked her ears a little, tuning into subtler sounds. Murmurings of trout and scratchings of crayfish, the wood sorrel flowers closing up to sleep. But when she turned her ears to the east, the Leshy's fur prickled and she sat up with a start. There was a sound that cut through the others: a high, mewling whine.

She crashed through the blackberry thicket and slowed in the oak wood, peering between the leaves. Two hairless cubs were kneeling over something, speaking to each other in their warbling language. Their faces were two sides of the same moon, both with hair the colour of winter chestnuts and eyes amber as fox.

The Leshy growled in her throat when she saw the basket of stolen berries next to them. She bared her teeth when she spied the furred body in the leaf litter, reddish gold and a black-tipped tail. But she froze when she saw the boy was using his weight to push two springs either side of an iron trap around the fox's leg. The Leshy settled into her hindquarters, watching, ready to pull off their arms and legs if they hurt her fox.

The jaws sprang open, easy as death, and the boy tore a strip from his shirt and used it to bind the leg. The girl drew the fox to her heart, as the Leshy had done when the fox was a cub and mewed for its dead mother. The girl rocked him in her arms and crooned words over him. The Leshy's eyes widened. This was the language of the hairless men, but in song it sounded different. It was the same tone that animals used to soothe their offspring, and the intonation she herself used when she sang back to the forest. The voice of trees, water, wind and earth. The boy pushed the berries to one side, and the girl put the fox in the basket, carefully. The Leshy came to herself and pushed her large, animal body through the bushes.

The boy cried out, pulling his torn shirt together as if it were armour. His sister clutched the basket to her and stepped in front of her brother, trembling as a poplar in the breeze. The Leshy drew her lips back to show the long, pointed eye-teeth she used to tear meat. The girl took in the Leshy's bristling fur, her snarl. Without breaking her gaze, she returned the snarl with one of her own. Her teeth were square and broken, but the Leshy dropped her fighting stance. No one had ever growled at the Leshy before.

The fox, bleary-eyed and seeking comfort, turned up his sharp snout and nosed into the girl's hand. His velvety nostrils flared as he took in her scent. The girl snuck her fingers through his fur and under his chin. A pink tongue darted between the sharp teeth, investigating the girl as gently as a bee in a flower. The Leshy froze and retracted her claws.

The Leshy's saucer eyes rolled between the girl-cub and the fox-cub. Slowly, the Leshy lifted a hairy arm, and offered her fingers to the girl to smell too. The cub, eyes wild and wary, leaned forward and took a deep sniff.

Memorial Days

Wayne Karlin

I will use the day to remember Dennis.

At the point from which I start to paddle, the channel is only a few yards wide and the water shallow and brown over a bottom of mud, pebbles, matted leaves and branches. Some of the branches scrape like fingernails along the kayak's bottom and an escort of panicked darters dance over the surface of the water, in front of and alongside me. The banks are tangled with bushes and holly and the branches of the sycamores and elms and oaks arch and interweave overhead. In the shaded spots the water is transparent, and where sun spots filter through the shifting leaves they touch off, like paint dissipating from the tip of a brush, amoebic milky shapes on the surface and when I shift my eyes off one of them and take in the surrounding water, swirled with fallen leaves, it turns into a shifting tan and white camouflage.

As the woods close around me, I feel bands of tension I haven't even been aware of loosen from my forehead and chest. The light that breaks through the lace of leaves runs along with me as I paddle, the sparkle awakening as if the brush of my sight on the water created it. As I round a bend I see a blue heron, large as a five year old child. It looks up, gives an impatient squawk and does its disjointed, mechanical-toy heron take-off, soaring from awkwardness to grace as it enters its element and wings downstream, following the cambering of the creek and staying low. It is his kingdom, and I call out that I am just a visitor, mean him no harm, something I'd learned from Dennis, picked up from a children's book Dennis had liked, though, even at eight years old a myth-maker, he had first claimed it as local legend.

I am in the country of childhood now, in a child's dream that I could enter through some portal in a tree or in a wardrobe, pass over into the shadowlands. Gliding into the country of memory, coached by the day's memorial purpose. I follow the heron's flight until the night I'd met Ashley and lost Dennis assembles for me, my perception conjugating to an endless flowing present tense; I am again in Bledsoe's Bar and Dennis is telling me he has joined the Marines and I am rigid with an anger that is partly envy and partly an anticipation of the grief I feel now.

How does your father feel about it, I ask him.

Dennis keeps grinning silently, through a wreath of smoke, through the thin curtain of marsh grass, through the scrim of heat-mist rising off the surface of the water. He leans forward, coming out of the mist and the bar room gloom, clarifying. In the strobing neon bar signs sometimes he looks like his Vietnamese mother, an Asian cast to his cheekbones and eyes, his hair black and straight, but he has his father's size, bulk and broad shoulders and sometimes he is taken for a Wesort, usurping the mix that flows in my own family's blood from the runaway Brit indentureds, renegade Piscataways and escaped African slaves who once found refuge together in the Southern Maryland marshes. He doesn't answer my question.

I don't blame him, I say. *He doesn't want you to become him.*

Dennis' grin widens. *What's wrong with my father?*

Same thing was wrong with mine.

Your dad was a better man because of Vietnam. It gave him the guts to check out when he had to.

It gave him the reason to do it. That fucking year in his life pressed like a lid on all the rest of his years.

The creek widens and the dip of the paddle propels me back to the slipping present. I pass further into marshland, the forest opening to acres of undulating cord grass, jeweled with dew-flecked spider webs and picketed here and there with looming hundred-foot sentinels of loblolly pine, some of them standing dead and white and skeletal. The tide line is a little low, exposing the muddied bottoms of the grass stalks. Clusters of small brown snails cling to the stalks and I remember how Dennis once told me that his mother would cook and eat the tiny snails that she chose to see as emissaries from her own shadowland of memories, shelled inhabitants of a Mekong she could sometimes transpose over Southern Maryland scenes, coax the water lilies into brilliant lotus blossoms that floated on the billowing green robes of water fairies, rooted in mud and petalling in sun. Whenever Dennis went fishing, he would gather snails for her, though when we were kids, he made me promise not to tell any of our classmates. It was one of the secrets that knit us, that existed to knit us, like our fantasy of the shadowlands, and Dennis' middle, Vietnamese, name that no one else could know.

Tough to be the children of myths, I say to Dennis.

Tough titty. The only way, my friend, to escape the legend, is to make your own legend.

The marsh stretches around me, the fetid smell of it thickening in my nostrils whenever my paddle brings up gobs of mud. I round a bend, paddle away from the tendrils of memories, my father's stories of his war floating into my memories of Dennis' mother, Xuân, and the secret name Dennis told me must never be pronounced, or a ghost would drown him. This marsh had been our Vietnam when we were kids, trying to be our fathers, humping the wetlands with plastic rifles and later BB guns, enduring the heat and insect bites. Though Dennis, more often than not, played being Viet Cong, his father's old enemies. I like winners, he said to me. The games we played, waiting impatiently for the chance to bring the real thing into our lives. I miss him, and I miss my father and the country I float through once again diffuses and transforms in the heat haze into that country whose name was never uttered except as the name of a war or the name of a curse. Vietnam-the-war drawn like a gauze veil over everything I –

and Dennis and his sister Tuyết and Ashley – saw, as if that were our inheritance.

I can no longer see bottom, only a ghost crest of wavering grass beneath the surface of the creek.

I dig the paddle in, left and right, finding a rhythm, the motion rocking me to another memory of my father: Jack had sneered at the kayak, called it a yuppie toy. The S.S. *Minnow*. You've gone over to the enemy, boy. I shut my eyes, my skim over the water the glide my father had taken into another country where I couldn't follow. No more than I could follow Dennis' Humvee as it rose impossibly on an expanding bubble of gas and flame and tipped into a scum-rimed, garbage-clogged canal running alongside a street in some shithole town in Anbar Province: my friend from this estuarine place where we had both grown up, drowning, as if a ghost had found his secret name. Drowning in that trash-filled, reed-choked alien water now somehow confluent to the creek upon which I have now come to commemorate him on this Memorial Day.

I paddle harder, racing against ghosts. In Bledsoe's Bar it is the night I lost Dennis and, within minutes of his telling me he would leave for the war, found the woman who would become Ashley and in my life. She turns and looks at me from across the marsh grass, from across the space between our tables in the barroom gloom, a slim, blond woman whose eyes flit past mine and then back and then don't look away. Her eyes are grey and full of intelligence, her face shadowed and then lit by the sputter of a neon Old Boh sign on the wall behind the bar. She flicks her tongue nervously at the beer foam on her lips and a little frisson runs through my veins, a jolt of recognition that for a time afterwards I will like to think of as a premonition, our future together folding back in time to touch and inform that moment. Though what I understand now is it was our fathers' war that linked us. The same unrequested history that tied me to Dennis. Filtered that night through the war waiting for Dennis. She smiles at me. I think I see her nod slightly, as if approving my words.

My anger at Dennis for going to the war. Dennis catches my stare. Sees what I see in it. Winks at Ruth, his girl that night, and then grins, swivels towards Ashley.

Darlene, I'd like you to meet my good friend Hunter.

My name's not Darlene.

Well, hell, I'm half right.

She stares at him. I can see her trying to repress a smile; Dennis' inevitable effect. *Why on Earth are you going into the Marines,* she asks him, then flushes. *I'm sorry. I wasn't eavesdropping.*

Dennis grins again, pats the empty chair next to mine.

Sure you were. Come on over. You kids were made for each other.

She smiles at me.

Is that right?

I hope so, I say, with no humour at all. She blinks quickly, a stalker-warning flickering in her eyes, and I smile, trying to silently reassure her that I am sane.

Come on over, Dennis says again.

You may not like what I have to say.

Hell, you already threw the chum in the water, honey.

He pats the seat next to me again.

Come over, sit on down. Speak your mind.

She hesitates a moment and then gives a what-the-hell shrug, rises, picks up her beer, joins us.

The question is, she says, *whether or not you really believe in the war.*

He will if he has to, I say.

Hey, I'm proud of him, we're fighting fanatics, Ruth says.

You know what the aim of fanaticism is, Ashley says.

My aim is fine, Dennis says. *Best thing about me.*

At least nobody's going to spit on him when he comes back, Ruth says.

I support the soldiers. Anyway, that's such an urban myth, Ashley says.

I had an uncle, Ruth says.

I have a father, Ashley says.

Support the troops, Dennis says, grinning wickedly. *Whoop, whoop, whoop. Support the troops. That's the trick. With stickers and bumpers and ribbons, oh my.*

He and Ruth begin to sing it.

Stickers and bumpers and ribbons, oh my.

Stickers and bumpers and ribbons, oh my.

Stickers and bumpers and ribbons, oh my.

Bullshit, Ashley says. She glares at me. *I support them by wanting to get them home safe.*

Sure thing, I say. I would have said anything to keep her next to me. To have her back. To have him back. I am mourning both of them. I'm in a fucking swamp mourning two losses. Though the distance between Ashley and me is only the distance of failed love and fading time. She is still alive, exists somewhere beyond the cage of my memories; Dennis is only the mist pierced like a tattered white curtain by the reeds around me.

Still, I lost them both to the war.

Your name is Hunter? Well, isn't that reassuring.

It's an old county name, I say defensively, and then think of another. *At least it's not Minor.*

Beer explodes from Dennis' nostrils. *Minor Dobson. 7th Grade. What a tool.*

Ashley giggles. *Minor? As in Major?*

That's right. Anyway what kind of name is Ashley? Lady Ashley? Your parents into Hemingway?

Fucking Hunter, Dennis says. *Like everyone in the world gets his references. Like anybody reads books.*

My father, Ashley says primly, *is a funeral director.*

Oh shit, Dennis says. *The General. I heard of him.* He salutes her.

Least I don't want to be a Hemingway character, Den, I say.

A flat-bottomed wooden skiff is anchored among the cord grass in

[228]

a small side stream that is hidden by the reeds until I am almost up on it. An Amish girl, in her bonnet and homespun cotton dress is standing in the bow, fishing with a bamboo pole; at the stern a straw-hatted, beardless boy sits baiting a hook. They could be brother and sister. Both are motionless; they fasten me into a silent past I want to keep wrapped around myself. As if complicit in the need, they ignore me. I am an impossible intrusion from a future century, an awkward slip in time. Seeing myself through their eyes. Through my Wesort eyes, my father would have said, calling up the occasional shifts in sight descendants of that blood mix supposedly experienced. Peripheral glimpses of the fragmented past that would suddenly float front and centre in my vision. An ability I never let myself believe in except when it was happening to me, and it only happened here, in this place my family had lived, in my father's words, since Christ was a corporal. *We've lived here since Christ was a Corporal*, I say to Ashley, and she smiles; it is a term, she tells me later, she has heard her father use.

An empty, dusty, bottle of Yoohoo in the stern of the Amish skiff fastens my eyes back to the present, floods me with a sense of relief that the Amish kids are really there, really here, really now.

'You kids were made for each other,' I assure the pair. They nod at me.

Here you go, Lady Ashes, Dennis says, passing a joint to her. She draws in the smoke, exhales, hands it to me and I put my lips where her lips were. We are both drunk, but not that much, and in the back seat of Dennis' Camry, the warm skin of her arm against mine, her hip pressed against mine, she smiles and presses in harder and when our eyes meet there is the hint of a promise between us that we both know is as delicate as a strand in a spider web bowed up in a breeze. Later Ashley would say it was only because of what I'd said about fathers and she was a soldier's daughter and we were talking about the war and it was Dennis' last night before the Marines that she had sat with me, and then, when Bledsoe's closed, went with us to the

[229]

Point. As if Dennis leaving for the war gave us a crazy kind of permission. As if instead of Dennis it was me acting out the cliché of grabbing at the quick of life before descending into the fire.

I turn the kayak into a slot in the saw grass, follow it back into forested country, gliding through a seemingly impassable curtain of reeds that I know is just a fringe. In the growing dusk I see my paddle trail a thread of phosphorescence in the water. I glide forward. The Camry barely stops when Dennis is out of the door whooping and running zigzag down a bluff over the river. By the time we catch up with him, he is already bare-assed and splashing in the water. *Ain't he beautiful,* Ruth chuckles, and runs down to join him. Ashley and I sit in the sand at the foot of the large concrete cross that marks the place the first colonists landed and I tell her inanely how they were welcomed warmly by the Piscataway Indians who thought to stick these hapless newcomers here between themselves and their Susquehannock enemies and she says yes, yes, she knows, and we hear Dennis and Ruth splashing in the river and we smoke again and we both know we are getting high not to lose inhibitions but to give us the excuse that we had done so. The cross stands ghostly, seemingly insubstantial in the night mist hovering over the river and I lean over to her or she leans over to me and we kiss and later, minutes or hours later, Ashley grins the same to-hell-with-it way she had before she'd jumped to our table in Bledsoe's and we go into the river, shifting, crystalline wisps of that mist weaving around and over us, beading on our bodies, sometimes parting and letting the full moon shine through to lay shifting, silvery scales on the black water. Her body rising out of that water to me, skin streaked with glows of phosphorescence and she laughs at the sight of me, at how much I want her, nothing minor there, she says, and when we come together I feel an estuarine blend of sensations I try to memorise even as they slip past: the cold of that river on my skin and the warmth inside her and the current pushing at our legs as she shudders and comes back to herself and pushes me away and we stand laughing, like delighted children, watching a luminescent cloud pulse out of me, ignited by the phosphorescence that always waits like ghosts in that dark water.

I push the bow of the kayak up a few inches onto the bank, and then get out and pull it to shore. Little has changed since the last time I was here. The pin oak stands in a hushed clearing. It is probably a hundred feet tall, and so thick two adults could not have wrapped their extended arms around it. It is a presence. Dennis and Tuyết had first taken me here when I was ten years old, the memory, like all my memories this Memorial Day, a palimpsest over the geography in front of my eyes now, past borne into borderless present. Shaded by the tree is a small, grass-covered hillock, about fifteen feet long and five feet high, swelling strangely out of otherwise flat ground; it is, according to Emmett Wheeler, a Native American burial mound. We had accepted his assessment when we were kids because we wanted it to be true; even at ten years old we recognised wishful thinking. But over the years we'd become more certain that their dad was correct, as we found buried arrowheads and faint cryptic symbols carved into the trunk of the tree, spirals and circles and squares, stretched out and their lines distorted by the tree's growth. Emmett had refused to report the site to the archaeologists at the college; he would not have, he said, whoever was buried there disturbed. One of the few times I saw him and Xuân Wheeler truly angry was when the three of us decided to dig into the mound, using our bare hands. I had gotten deep enough to close my hand around something smooth and long and narrow that could have been a bone or a stick, when they caught us at it. Emmett screamed. But it was the tight-lipped expression on Xuân Wheeler's face, her silent rage, the slight tremble in her hands, that stopped us cold, an expression I had never taken as literal until that moment. A chill went through my blood. Tuyết began to cry.

But Dennis, staring at his mother, just grinned. Man, he said, patting the mound, when I die, this is the place.

Said as a joke, a way to annoy his mother, I had thought. He loved to tease her, and – most of the time – she loved being teased by him.

But over the years, he had repeated that request whenever we came here, the mound and the tree always the end point for all our games, though Tuyết stopped coming with us after that day. The last time he said it to me was after boot camp and just before he was deployed, the two of us drinking cans of Old Boh beer and ceremonially tossing the cans onto the mound, our backs against the tree. It was a promise that of course I could not fulfill. Per the Wheeler family tradition, half his ashes had been interred at St. Inigoes Church and the rest scattered over the river. And even then, I wasn't sure if he was being serious or just being Dennis, presenting me with a dramatic last request before the war, an ironic acknowledgement of our shared vocabulary from the war movies that informed our childhood and that he was going to act out with his own life. Dennis the Menace.

I have brought a small knapsack with me. I unsling it at the base of the tree and draw out a small, blue tablecloth. I spread it between two knotted roots that disappear underground for a few feet and then muscle up out of the earth again as they reach the burial mound. I reach back into the knapsack and pull out the rest of the objects I've brought: a framed photo of Dennis in his green and gold coloured gown at our high school graduation; I'd cropped myself out of the picture. A can of Old Boh beer. Two mandarin oranges and two apples. A Hershey chocolate bar. A small bowl. A hand spade. A stack of hell money and a bundle of incense sticks I'd bought from the Asian grocery in town.

I rest the photo against the trunk of the tree, its right edge touching one of those connecting roots, pick up the small bowl, go to the mound and spade up some dirt and fill the bowl. I place it in front of the photo, and then arrange the fruit and chocolate on one side of the tablecloth, the can of Old Boh on the other.

Growing up, I was always invited to the Wheelers around mid-July – whenever the fifteenth day of the seventh month in the lunar calendar fell – when Xuân Wheeler performed Trung Nguyen, the Day of Wandering Souls, ceremonies at a table covered with food, fruit, flowers, a small plate covered with coins and dollar bills, and smoldering incense sticks, their sweet sharp scent diffusing into the air, mixing with and sharpening the heavy scent of the bougainvillea she'd planted around the house. The table was set outside. It was the custom to feed the hungry ghosts who were said to wander the earth that day. But wise not to bring them into your house. There were hundreds of thousands of wandering souls left from the war, Emmett Wheeler had told us, the Vietnamese soldiers missing in action or civilians killed with no place nor family to give them rest, all doomed to roam and starve because their remains were never recovered and buried in ancestral ground. Xuân Wheeler's brother was one of them, Emmett once told us; his name had been given to Dennis. The part of the ceremony we three kids liked best was its ending, when Xuân and Emmett would toss the food and money on the table at us, and we would, per the custom, fight each other for it. Enthusiastically. Having grown up Catholic, I liked to imagine being in church and watching parishioners punch each other out as they scrambled for the wafer. This is my body, fight for it. We would wait anxiously while Xuân Wheeler prayed. Once the incense sticks burned down, she would kneel, her hands in front of her chest, bowing until her forehead touched the ground, weeping for her brother, burning a stack of hell money to send to him. But as soon as she looked up and spotted us, she would beam, her face transforming instantly. She would hold up the money plate and start by flinging the coins and bills at us, and then start pelting us with sugar cane, oranges, and chocolate bars. We grabbed at the offerings, punching, pushing, screeching with excitement while she and Emmett Wheeler laughed their asses off. Welcome to V.C. Halloween, Dennis would always whisper to me, at some point.

I try now to remember and imitate what I would see Xuân Wheeler do as she prayed at that table for lost souls.

I unwrap and light the incense, holding the bundle in one hand and fanning the flame with the other. Pressing the incense between both palms, I close my eyes and slowly bring it up to my forehead and then down again, three times. *The only way, my friend, to escape the legend, is to make your own legend.* I stick the bottoms of the incense sticks into the bowl. I am culturally appropriating like hell, and probably offending both sundry Vietnamese hungry ghosts and whatever Native American spirits rest in that mound. Dennis was not a wandering soul. Not technically. His remains had been returned and commemorated. The ghost I was bringing here was the ghost of our childhood. Dennis would understand. We made things our own. We were our own country. What I always took and treasured from being invited yearly to that wandering souls ceremony was the same gratitude I had felt when Dennis and Tuyết sealed me to themselves by bringing me here, to this secret and sacred place. It is the same way I felt when Dennis told me his secret name.

I watch as the incense sticks burn down, their long fingers transmuted into fragile ash replicas of their original form. A breeze picks up the ash and scatters it.

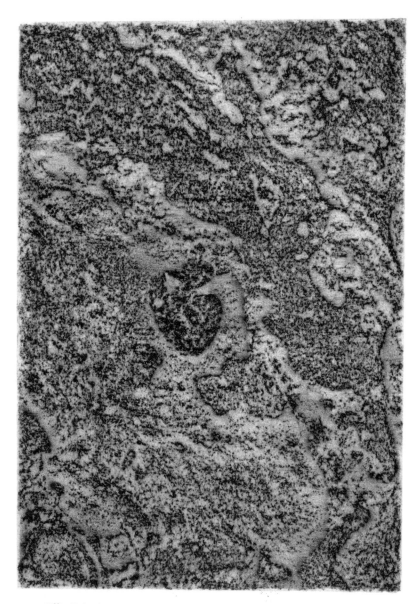

Effie Paleologou
From the *Microcosms* series: Rubbing #3,
Graphite on paper, 2013–17

Afterword

What do the birds say?

'There is nothing intelligent to say about a massacre', writes Kurt Vonnegut in *Slaughterhouse-Five*. 'Everybody is supposed to be dead, to never say anything or want anything ever again. Everything is supposed to be very quiet after a massacre, and it always is, except for the birds.

'And what do the birds say? All there is to say about a massacre, things like *"Poo-tee-weet?"'*

Perhaps there is nothing intelligent to say about 2020. To say *'Poo-tee-weet?'* in a world that feels as fictional and as fantastical as Vonnegut's novel – which ranges through space and time from the 1945 firebombing of Dresden to the alien planet Tralfamadore – is not to deny, or to mock, the seriousness of the crises we're in. It is not to give up on reality, or to invite despair. But during the long, strange months of lockdown, when skies cleared of vapour trails and motorways became eerily silent, what many people commented on was the sound of birdsong. Once the omnipresent roar of human activity was suppressed, the quiet, insistent language of birds bubbled back into people's consciousness. That reminder of the living world, still present underneath – and despite – everything that is burying it, increasingly seems to make more sense than the clamour of human noise: the frenzied rationalisations of political commentators who feel the ground shifting under their feet; the demagogic bellowing of populist leaders everywhere; the polarising narratives of social media. A fleeting moment of quietness – like the silence after a massacre – allowed us, briefly, to hear something else. Birdsong tells its own story.

Poo-tee-weet.

The Editors, Autumn 2020

Contents

Dark Mountain: Issue 18 – FABULA

Audio recordings

To mark this special issue of uncivilised fiction, we asked eight of the contributors to *Dark Mountain: Issue 18 – FABULA* to record audio versions of the stories they contributed to the book.

'Three Buzzing Boys' by **Julia Blackburn**
'Meeting Jeff Bezos' by **Siana Fitzjohn**
'Armadillo', 'Constant Comment' and 'Rabbits' by **Kim Goldberg**
'The Gramarye' by **Kirsty Logan**
'Mehel' by **Micheál Mac Gearailt**
'For Whom It Should Remain Silent' by **Eric Roberston**
'Killing Snakes' by **Conrad Schumaker**
'Flux' by **Luke Winter**

You can listen to them online at **dark-mountain.net/issue-18-fabula-audio**

Or by scanning the code below.

Mountaineers

Sarah Ainslie is a freelance photographer whose work is inspired by living and working in London's East End. At present she is documenting the more liminal edges of London where urban and rural life collide, and where the edges of capitalist development clash with the detritus of abandoned communities and industry. **sarahainslie.com**

Sunandini Banerjee is Senior Editor and Graphic Designer at Seagull Books in Calcutta. A digital-collage artist whose work has been exhibited in India and internationally, as well as a translator, Sunandini also teaches editing and book design at the Seagull School of Publishing. She lives and works in Calcutta.

Fiona Banner aka The Vanity Press is a British artist, who was shortlisted for the Turner Prize in 2002. Her work encompasses sculpture, drawing, installation and text. She is well known for her early works in the form of 'wordscapes', written transcriptions of the frame-by-frame action in Hollywood war films. Her work has been exhibited in the Museum of Modern Art, New York and Hayward Gallery, London, among other museums and galleries.

Kevin Bell's work explores how cultural values and aspirations shape our experience of landscape. His research is informed by growing up in the western United States. He earned a BA in history from Bowdoin College and completed an MFA in painting from the University of Oregon. Kevin is the Director and an Associate Professor at the School of Art, University of Montana in Missoula, where he lives with his family.

Julia Blackburn was born in London in 1948, the daughter of the poet Thomas Blackburn and the painter Rosalie de Meric. She lives in Suffolk and sometimes in northern Italy. She has written many books of poetry and non-fiction, the most recent being *Time Song* (2019). She is currently working on a book called *Dreaming the Karoo*, which has changed shape because she had to return from the Karoo in a hurry in late March. 'Three Buzzing Boys' was originally commissioned by BBC Radio 4.

William Bock is an interdisciplinary artist working between Ireland and the UK, exploring the connections between people and their environments. His work encompasses photography, painting, sound recording, performance and installation. Bock is winner of the Sustainability First 2020 Art prize, co-founder of artist group *Dig Collective* and member of *Wilderness Art Collective*.

adrienne maree brown is the author of *Pleasure Activism: The Politics of Feeling Good*, *Emergent Strategy: Shaping Change, Changing Worlds* and the co-editor of *Octavia's Brood: Science Fiction from Social Justice Movements*. She is the cohost of the *How to Survive the End of the World* and *Octavia's Parables* podcasts. adrienne is rooted in Detroit.

Petra Carlson was born in 1975 in Kauniainen, Finland. She graduated with a Bachelor of Fine Arts from ECAL in Lausanne and continues to live in Switzerland. Her monochrome drawings are inspired by our world, a place where we are often stranded and where hope and despair surround us.

Mike Cipra has lived and written in landscapes ranging from Death Valley to the old-growth redwood forests of northern California. He's looking for representation and a publisher for his first novel, *Enviro*. Mike is honoured to be included among the writers, artists, and thinkers involved in the Dark Mountain Project. mikecipra.com

Siana Fitzjohn lives near Ōtautahi in Aotearoa (New Zealand) with her dog, sheep, bunny, pig and parents. She is a civilly disobedient environmental activist, most recently with Extinction Rebellion. Siana found a home for her writing in *Dark Mountain*, and believes in the power of dark humour to combat fatigue and help us push on through the glorious mess.

Luna Mrozik Gawler is a transdisciplinary artist, researcher and facilitator interested in the role of live art in multispecies worlding and future making. Based in Birrarung-ga/Melbourne, their work explores the intersections, ethics and entanglements of bodies and has featured at multiple festivals. Luna's writing has appeared in a range of texts including *ROAR*, *Going Down Swinging*, and *Bombay Gin*. lunamrozikgawler.com.au

Kim Goldberg is the author of eight books. Her latest is *Devolution* (Caitlin Press, 2020), a collection of poems and fables of ecotastrophe, including the three fables shared here. Kim lives and wanders on Vancouver Island, where rabbits are proliferating. Twitter: @KimPigSquash

Nick Hayes is a graphic novelist, illustrator and author of *The Book of Trespass*, out now. It is a non-fiction exploration of land rights in England, told through trespassing the estates of the lords, dukes, media magnates and private corporations that own England. He currently lives in London, but might be on a barge by time this book is in your hands.

Nick Hunt is a writer, editor and co-director of the Dark Mountain Project. He is the author of two travel books, *Where the Wild Winds Are* and *Walking the Woods and the Water*, and a work of gonzo ornithology, *The Parakeeting of London*. He is currently finishing a third travel book and working on his first novel. nickhuntscrutiny.com

Neale Inglenook is a contributing editor for the online edition of the Dark Mountain Project, and his fiction and essays can be found in the pages of its books. He lives on the California coast he grew from, and is at work on a novel rooted in this landscape's cities and wild places.

Cynan Jones' novels and stories have been published in over twenty countries and in many anthologies and magazines including *Granta* and *The New Yorker*. He has also written stories for radio, a screenplay for the crime drama *Hinterland*, and a collection of tales for children. His latest book is *Stillicide*.

Jon Jost, born in 1943, has been making films and photography since 1963. He has some forty feature-length films and numerous films to his credit.

Nicholas Kahn & Richard Selesnick are a collaborative artist team who work primarily in the fields of photography and installation art, specialising in fictitious histories set in the past or future. Kahn & Selesnick have participated in exhibitions worldwide and have work in over twenty collections. In addition, they have published three books with Aperture Press: *Scotlandfuturebog*, *City of Salt* and *Apollo Prophecies*.

Wayne Karlin has published eight novels and three works of non-fiction. His latest novel *A Wolf by the Ears* won the Juniper Prize for Fiction for 2019. In addition, he has received two fellowships from the National Endowment for the Arts, the Paterson Prize in Fiction, and the Vietnam Veterans of American Excellence in the Arts Award.

Paul Kingsnorth is co-founder of the Dark Mountain Project. His novel *Alexandria* is published in February 2021. paulkingsnorth.net

Kathryn Kuitenbrouwer is the author of the novels *All The Broken Things*, *Perfecting*, and *The Nettle Spinner* as well as the story collection, *Way Up*. Her short fiction, creative non-fiction, poetry, and essays have been published in various journals including *Granta*, *Storyville*, *The Walrus*, *The Lifted Brow*, and *The Letters Page*. She lives in the countryside in Canada where she is obsessed with grasses, which she both collects and scythes. Kuitenbrouwer holds a PhD from the University of Toronto and teaches creative writing at Colorado College, the University of Guelph, and the University of Toronto.

Kirsty Logan is a professional daydreamer. She is the author of two novels, *The Gloaming* and *The Gracekeepers*, and three story collections, *Things We Say in the Dark*, *A Portable Shelter* and *The Rental Heart & Other Fairytales*. She lives in Glasgow with her wife and their rescue dog. She has tattooed toes.

Johanna Lohrengel is an illustrator, storyteller and former social worker whose work explores reciprocal relationships with nature and children. Her art tells stories of people who dare to dream, to play and to take care of each other – against the odds of the speed of modern living. She is based on a community homestead in northern Latvia. johannalohrengel.com

Micheál Mac Gearailt is a farmer without a farm from the west of Ireland. A lover of mountains, history and literature, he has worked as an archaeologist, chef, rock-climbing instructor, drama teacher and construction worker, amongst other things. He is currently a prospective student of some university somewhere.

Luisa-Maria MacCormack is a fine artist and feminist educator. Working across a range of media, including painting, drawing, sculpture and printmaking, her work challenges and explores the difficult questions surrounding our gendered creative histories. She confronts issues of spirituality, supernatural and mythic traditions, sexuality, the body, belief and the evolution of ritual. She's a founding member of London Drawing Group.

Ekow Manuar was raised in Accra, Ghana. He studied in the US and Sweden in the disciplines of Political and Sustainability Science. Manuar intertwines his knowledge of development and environment to formulate trajectories that inform the future he envisions. His stories are of the people of West Africa, from now, till the brink of existence. medium.com/@abdallahsmith06

Mark Martin lives in Brooklyn but grew up in England. He is the managing editor at Verso Books. His fiction has appeared in *The Manchester Review*, *Dark Mountain*, *Storgy*, and *The Missouri Review* (forthcoming). He is the editor of an anthology of climate change fiction, *I'm With the Bears*.

Jason Massot is a film-maker based in London. His films have been screened at the Institute of Contemporary Arts in London, Edinburgh International Film Festival, International Documentary Film Festival Amsterdam and the Whitstable Biennale. His documentaries have been shown on BBC, Channel 4 and Discovery.

Bethan McFadden is a fine artist and illustrator based in London. Previous projects include two exhibitions of life-size drawings and sculptures of endangered animals, a residency in a wild animal refuge in Bolivia, and an exhibition of abstract ink and pencil works based on the impermanent nature of the mind. bethanmcfadden.com

Effie Paleologou is a London-based visual artist, whose work has been exhibited nationally and internationally and is held in collections such as the Victoria and Albert Museum in London and the National Museum of Contemporary Art in Athens.

Bridget Pitt is a South African author, environmental activist and artist, who has published poetry, short fiction, three novels and non-fiction. Her work has been shortlisted for several awards. Her work has been published in Canada, the UK, South Africa, and on international online platforms. Find out more at thelesserspottedauthor.com

Joanna Pocock is a writer currently living in London. *Surrender*, a hybrid memoir-travelogue about the American West, won the Fitzcarraldo Editions Essay Prize in 2018. It has since been published in the UK, Canada and the US. Spanish and French editions are forthcoming. Her words have appeared in *The Los Angeles Times*, *The Nation*, *The New Statesman*, *Orion*, *The Spectator* and *The Times Literary Supplement*. Joanna teaches Creative Writing at the University of the Arts, London.

Eric Robertson is a Dark Mountain editor and teaches in the Honors College at the University of Utah. He's a queer ecologist exploring how non-reproductive bodies shape the stories told about land use and human ecology.

Caroline Ross is a taichi instructor and artist using and teaching natural, found and foraged art materials. She migrates seasonally between a tiny boat on a Thames island, two huts in a cove and a tent in the woods. Her art can be found in seven of the Dark Mountain books and online at **carolineross.co.uk** and Instagram.com/foundandground

Sophie Shillito writes about spirit of place, palimpsests, and micro-histories. She is the author of two books: *All The Little Places* is a haunting poetic-prose tapestry of fairytale fragments; *Love From Kew* is an imaginative scrapbook of scribbled postcard stories. Sophie lives in London. She likes mudlarking and mountains. sophieshillito.com

Conrad Shumaker grew up on a cattle ranch/cotton farm outside Tucson, Arizona. He has recently retired from the University of Central Arkansas, where he taught classes in American literatures and cultures. He now writes, gardens, and raises chickens in a house he built in the woods of Arkansas.

Shirley Snow is a young London-based artist. She is due to study Film and TV at the Edinburgh College of Art in autumn 2020. She mostly works independently, making short, quiet, observational films as well as chapbooks consisting of found images and her own writing.

Born in 1945, **Lena Spindler** is a Swedish artist, astrologer and interior designer who spent most of her life living and working between London and West Cork, Ireland. Through weaving, painting and photography Lena captured the fleeting moments in nature, the subconscious world of dreams and the influence of the planets in our lives.

Shaun Tan grew up in Perth and works as an artist, writer and film-maker in Melbourne. He is best known for illustrated books that deal with social and historical subjects through dream-like imagery, widely translated throughout the world and enjoyed by readers of all ages. Shaun is the recipient of an Academy Award for the short animated film *The Lost Thing*, the prestigious Astrid Lindgren Memorial Award in Sweden and the Kate Greenaway Medal in the UK.

Jack Fawdry Tatham is an artist based in the UK. His work combines observational drawing and traditional etching with an exploration of the kinship between humans and nature. Jack works as a tutor at the Royal Drawing School where he completed his post-grad in 2017. He also looks after bees in central London. jackfawdrytatham.uk

Tom Walsh has fought wildfires, built hiking trails, and been a newspaper reporter and editor. He's lived for a spell throughout the US, England, New Zealand, and Bolivia. He now calls Sausalito, California home. As the world's attention span shortens, he's gained an interest in flash fiction.

John Weeden comes from New York City and grew up with a mother and brother who were artists. He studied sculpture at university, turned more towards painting soon after, and continues to do both. He has long been most interested in the ritual process of creation, how we create, how we get entangled and the emergence of works. He lives with his wife and children in Santiago de Compostela, Spain. johnweeden.com

Romy Tara Wenzel is a writer and artist in Melukerdee country, Tasmania. She explores mythology and ecology through an animist perspective. In her spare time she forages for wild pigments and clay, weaves baskets and plants acorns. Instagram @the_quiet_wilds

Philip Webb Gregg was born in the hills of southern Spain and raised by a community of activists, rebels and rogues. These days he makes a mostly honest living by making things up and writing them down. He lives in the flatlands of Cambridge and dreams of mountains. philipwebbgregg.com

Luke Winter likes to help stories happen. He has made his living as a writer since 2014 by busking stories-on-demand in the street with a typewriter across Europe and the US. He now lives in Scotland where he runs a small press at prancepress.

com, and helps others to write their own stories. This is the first time he's been published by Dark Mountain and that makes him very happy.
storiesforstrangers.com

Lynsey Wright grew up in the Midlands of England before moving to London to earn her degrees in Journalism and Creative Writing. She worked as a freelance writer whilst travelling the world and subsequently relocated to Las Vegas. She now lives in Central London and is working on her first novel.

Acknowledgements

'Bears with Lawyers' by Shaun Tan. Extract from *Tales from the Inner City* by Shaun Tan. Copyright ©2018 Shaun Tan. Reproduced by permission of Walker Books Ltd, London, SE11 5HJ. walker.co.uk

'Oxen' by Cynan Jones. Copyright ©2020 Cynan Jones. A new story, original to this issue of *Dark Mountain*. Printed by permission of the author and his agent, A.M. Heath & Co Ltd.

'the river' by adrienne maree brown. Originally published in *Octavia's Brood: Science Fiction Stories from Social Justice Movements* (AK Press, 2015)

SUBSCRIBE TO
DARK MOUNTAIN

Since 2009, we have made Dark Mountain a home for the work of writers, thinkers and artists exploring the unknown territory beyond the Pale of an unravelling civilisation. This project has taken many forms, but at its heart are books like this.

Everything we have published has been made possible through the support and generosity of our readers. At first, this was a case of hundreds of you joining in with our crowdfunding campaigns. Now, we're asking for a more ongoing form of support.

Take out a subscription to Dark Mountain and you will get each issue as soon as it comes out, at a lower price than anywhere else. You will also be giving us the security we need to continue producing these books.

To read more about the different levels of subscription, please visit:

dark-mountain.net/subscriptions

DaRk MOUNTAIN
MAIL ORDER

Back issues in print

Walking On Lava
Selected Works for
Uncivilised Times
(2017)
US paperback
£15.99

Uncivilisation
The Dark
Mountain
manifesto (2009)
Revised paperback ed.
£5.99

issue sixteen
(Autumn 2019)
hardback
£19.99

issue seventeen
(Spring 2020)
hardback
£16.99

All back issues available as pdf downloads *from £3.00 ea.*

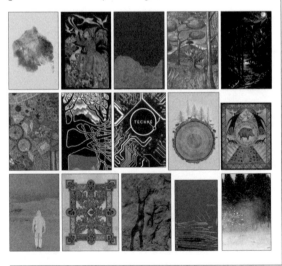

**From the
Mourning
of the World**
The first Dark Mountain
LP (2013)
12 inch vinyl £14
Download £10

{Reading the Ashes}
The second Dark
Mountain LP (2015)
Download £7

Also available guest publications from
the Dark Mountain team please visit:
dark-mountain.net/shop

Roll of honour

The publication of this book is made possible by the support of subscribers to the Dark Mountain Project. The following subscribers have provided financial support beyond the call of duty. We are very grateful for their belief in our work, and for that of all our subscribers across the world.

Bob Archer
Keith Badger
Kay and Wahhab
    Baldwin
Jeff Blackburn
Carolee Bol
Paula Boyle
Bruce Campbell
Sandra Carey
Ben Carpenter
Jonas Caufield
Theo Clarke
Kathleen Connolly
Peter Culp
Darius Cuplinskas
Kate Davis
Brook Dickson and
    Kurt Navratil
Alexa de Ferranti
Geoffrey Fischer
Simeon Gallu
Jack Gates-Browne
Alexander Grant
Claudia Grati
Jan Ernst de Groot
Christopher Hall

Colin Harper
James Heal
Rebecca Henderson
Victoria Hill
Ann Hine
Henrietta Hitchings
Christoph Höhn
Rachel Holstead
Michael Hughes
Andrew Hurley
Mary Strong Jackson
Erik Jacobs and
    Dina Rudick
    (Anthem Multimedia)
Atlantis Johnson
Andrew Junius
Max Kloosterman
Rebecca A. Knittle
Lark
Elizabeth Lindley-Davis
Jennifer Loewen
Shabehram Lohrasbe
Deirdre McAdams
Peter McDonald
William Maxwell
Johan Meylaerts

Brian Midtbo
Todd Moore
Sarah Murray
Stephen Nally
Noor Ney
S. Nate Pochan
Simon de Quincey
Johnny Rath
Bonnitta Roy
Douglas Scott
Jen Scott
Sara Solnick
Susie Unseld
Emily Veitch
Hans Vermaak and
    Eileen Moyer
Celia Fulton Walden
Elizabeth Watson
Gregory Webster
John Weeden (Green
    Chi Foundation)
Jacob Williams
Julia Winiarski
John W. Wolf
Robin Zykin

Published by the Dark Mountain Project 2020
dark-mountain.net

ISBN 978-0-9955402-9-3

Editors
Nick Hunt
Eric Robertson
Philip Webb Gregg

Art Editor
Joanna Pocock

Production
Nick Hunt

Proofreader
Hattie Pierce

Assistant Readers
Hattie Pierce
M.E. Rolle

Editorial Assistant
Ava Osbiston

Online editor
Charlotte Du Cann

Distribution
Mark Watson

Associate Publishers
Erik Jacobs and
Dina Rudick

MIX
Paper from
responsible sources
FSC® C013056
FSC
www.fsc.org

Typesetting by
Bracketpress

Printed and bound by
TJ Books Ltd.,
Padstow, PL28 8RW

Cover Art
Fiona Banner aka The Vanity Press
Arial (sinking), American Garamond,
Oil on found painting, 2019.

In this series of paintings Fiona Banner aka The Vanity Press reflects on a period of suspended animation and future uncertainty. The central concern of her practice is the exploration of language and communication; here she focuses on their breakdown. Banner has returned to a type of figurative painting, a tradition she rejected some years ago, turning instead to verbal language as a way of making pictures. In these works she presents a series of interventions to found genre paintings: seascapes.

She has painted out the original subject, mighty seafaring vessels, battleships and destroyers, replacing them instead with black full stops.
All images © Fiona Banner aka
The Vanity Press

Frontispiece and final page
Shirley Snow
Front and back cover of Shirley Snow's chapbook, *I'm Writing from a Distance,* 2020, which uses image combination inspired by Batia Suter's work on visual association.

FABULA

Dark Mountain

Issue 18

Autumn 2020

The Dark Mountain Project